Contents

C000265528

Introduction

Tackling Multiple Choice questions

Multiple choice questions form part of the exam for your second unit in the modular GCSE maths specification. This book has plenty of practice questions to help you get used to multiple choice questions and the technique involved. It also has two practice papers laid out like the real exam to get you ready for the big day.

The multiple choice questions in the exam consist of the question, and then five possible answers. Only one of these will be the correct answer but sometimes the other four will have been chosen in such a way that the correct answer is not immediately obvious.

There are some important things to remember about the multiple choice part of your exam

- The exam is half an hour long and has 25 questions, so you have just over a minute for each question.

- This means you do not want to waste a lot of time on one question – if you are unsure about the answer, leave it and come back to it later.

- Do try to answer every question, even if you have to guess, as there is no penalty for marking the wrong answer.

- There will always be only one correct answer, and if you select more than one, you will get no marks for that question.

- You are allowed to change your mind, but because you will not get any marks if more than one answer is picked, make sure that you erase your previous answers. If you are doing an on-screen or Optical Mark Reader (OMR) test, make sure you are familiar with what to do if you wish to change your answer.

- If you are doing the OMR test make sure you have the right type of pencil (HB) a good eraser, and that you fill in the circle completely.

Helpful tips for answering multiple choice questions

- You can break down the sorts of questions you will come across into four types:
  1. Questions you can easily answer
  2. Questions where some of the answers are not sensible
  3. Questions where an estimate will be good enough to identify the correct answer
  4. Questions where you really do not know the answer – these are the ones worth guessing.

- You can often work out which answer is the correct one without actually doing the calculation - you will find in many questions that the sensible choices are limited, and you can improve your chances by ruling out the obviously wrong answers.

- If that doesn't work, try to estimate what the answer would be and look for the answer that is closest to that estimate.

- Answers will not follow a pattern but there are likely to be similar numbers for each letter choice. i.e.there will be about 5 As, 5 Bs etc. This might help you when you have to guess an answer.
- It is unusual for three consecutive answers to be the same.

Each topic has only a limited number of ways of being tested. Make sure you do plenty of multiple choice examples so that you know the various ways a topic can be tested. Also, practice complete tests to get familiar with the timings.

The best method for doing a multiple choice exam is to

- Work through, answering only the questions you are sure about and can do quickly. Make a note of the numbers for the questions that you are leaving for later.
- Now check how much time is left and how many questions need answering

If the test is done on-line, you will need to keep a note of the questions that have been left for later.

Examples

Some questions can be answered by estimating.

1 What is 3.21×9.7?

    A 311.37   **B** 5.136   **C** 30.137   **D** 51.36   **E** 31.137

The answer must be about $3.2 \times 10 = 32$
It must have a total of $2 + 1 = 3$ decimal places.
The last digit must come from 1×7 (the last digits of the numbers).

Hence the answer can only be **C** or **E**.
The estimate of 10 is 0.3 more than 9.7 so 32 is about $0.3 \times 32 = 0.9$, too big.
The answer is **E**.

2 The bearing of A from B is 224. What is the bearing of B from A?

    A 134   **B** 044   **C** 314   **D** 404   **E** 224

Bearings are always between 000 and 360 so **D** is not a possibility.
The direction of B from A involves a half turn from the A from B direction.
Hence the answer must be **B**

Sometimes you can use the answers.

1 The solution of $2x^2 - x - 1 = 0$ is

    A 1 and 0.5   **B** 1 and -0.5 **C** -1 and 0.5   **D** 2 and 1   **E** -1 and -0.5

You can spot one answer is obviously $x = 1$
The answer can only be **A**, **B** or **D**.

Now test the other answers. $x = 2$ means $2 \times 2^2 - 2 - 1 = 5$ and this does not work
                           $x = 0.5$ means $2 \times (0.5)^2 - 0.5 - 1$ which is negative

This only leaves $x = -0.5$ and **B** as the answer.

2 Factorise $3x^2 - 5x + 2$

A $(3x - 2)(x - 1)$ **B** $(3x + 2)(x - 1)$ **C** $(3x - 1)(x + 2)$
D $(3x - 1)(x - 2)$ **E** $(3x + 2)(x + 1)$

When multiplied out, all answers give $3x^2$ as the first term so that does not help.
Only **A**, **D** and **E** give $+2$ as the last term so the answer must be one of these.
It cannot be **E** because that will not give a negative middle term
D gives $-7x$ and **A** gives $-5x$ as the middle term. So **A** is the answer.

Sometimes you can use the diagrams.

Some questions often have a diagram.

Although these are not accurately drawn they are usually good enough to know if the answer is acute, obtuse or reflex if the question involves an angle.

1 Work out the area of this trapezium.

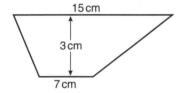

A $40 \, \text{cm}^2$ **B** $10 \, \text{cm}^2$ **C** $33 \, \text{cm}^2$ **D** $21 \, \text{cm}^2$ **E** $45 \, \text{cm}^2$

The answer must be smaller than the rectangle $15 \, \text{cm} \times 3 \, \text{cm} = 45 \, \text{cm}^2$
The answer must be larger than the rectangle $7 \, \text{cm} \times 3 \, \text{cm} = 21 \, \text{cm}^2$

The only possible answer is **C** $33 \, \text{cm}^2$

2

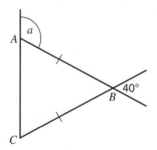

What is the size of angle a?

A $130°$ **B** $110°$ **C** $100°$ **D** $60°$ **E** $40°$

The angle is obviously larger than $90°$.
Hence **D** and **E** are not possible.
$130°$ would mean angle $CAB = 50°$ (angles on a straight line) so **A** is not the answer.
Try $100°$. Then both base angles would be $80°$ and the angle at B only $20°$, so this not the answer.
This only leaves **B** $110°$ which is the correct answer.

3

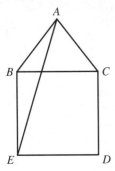

ABC is an equilateral triangle. *BCDE* is a square.
What is the size of angle *AED*?

A 45°   **B** 60°   **C** 75°   **D** 30°   **E** 15°

The diagram may not be accurately drawn but clearly angle *AED* is more than 45° and nearer to 90°
That only leaves **B** and **C** as sensible answers.
It is not the same as the angles in the equilateral triangle, so **C** 75° is the answer.

4

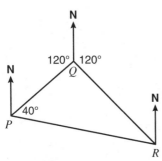

What is the bearing of *P* from *R*?

A 080°   **B** 100°   **C** 120°   **D** 260°   **E** 280°

Imagine standing at *R* facing North. To face *P* you must turn clockwise more than 270°
Hence the answer is **E** 280°. All the other answers are too small..

6 Number

6.1 Properties of whole numbers

1 Which number is a factor of 24?

A 48

B 6

C 36

D 16

E 20

2 Which number is a factor of 81?

A 18

B 243

C 0

D 11

E 3

3 Which number is a factor of 30?

A 10

B 90

C 16

D 20

E 9

4 Which number is a multiple of 12?

A 3

B 6

C 24

D 8

E 4

5 Which number is a multiple of 15?

A 1

B 5

C 3

D 45

E 10

6 Here is a list of numbers.

2, 5, 6, 8, 24

Which two of these numbers are factors of 12?

A 6 and 8

B 2 and 6

C 2 and 8

D 8 and 24

E 2 and 5

7 Here is a list of numbers.

3, 4, 5, 7, 10

Which two of these numbers are factors of 45?

A 5 and 10

B 5 and 7

C 3 and 5

D 3 and 7

E 4 and 10

8 Here is a list of numbers.

2, 4, 6, 7, 9, 10

Which two of these numbers are prime?

A 2 and 7

B 2 and 9

C 7 and 10

D 4 and 7

E 2 and 6

9 Which are common factors of 12 and 18?

   A 4 and 3

   B 2 and 3

   C 3 and 9

   D 6 and 9

   E 2 and 4

10 How many factors does the number 24 have?

   A 4

   B 6

   C 8

   D 2

   E 10

6.2 Multiplication and division of directed numbers

1 Work out $(+2) \times (-5)$

   A $+7$

   B $+10$

   C -3

   D -7

   E -10

2 Work out $(-7) \times (-7)$

   A $+14$

   B 0

   C -49

   D $+49$

   E -14

3 What is $(+20) \div (-5)$?

   A -4

   B $+4$

   C $+15$

   D -15

   E -5

4 Work out $(-14) \div (-2)$

   A -7

   B $+7$

   C -16

   D $+16$

   E -16

5 What is the product of -5 and 3?

   A -8

   B -2

   C $+2$

   D -15

   E $+15$

6 Work out the missing number.

$$(+15) \times ? = -45$$

   A -60

   B -30

   C $+30$

   D $+3$

   E -3

7 What is the product of -7 and -9?

   A $+16$

   B $+63$

   C -63

   D $+2$

   E -16

8 What is $(+72) \div (-9)$?

   A -8

   B $+8$

   C -81

   D $+63$

   E $+81$

9 Work out the missing number.

$$? \div (-2) = +4$$

A $+8$

B -6

C -3

D -8

E $+6$

10 What is $(-32) \div (-8)$?

A -4

B $+40$

C $+4$

D -24

E -40

6.3 Squares, cubes

1 Work out 4^2

A 16

B 8

C 6

D 12

E 42

2 What is $\sqrt{64}$?

A 32

B 8

C 16

D 4

E 128

3 What is $(-12)^2$?

A -144

B -24

C 24

D -10

E 144

4 Work out $\sqrt[3]{125}$

A 72.5

B 5

C 25

D -5

E 4

5 Work out $\sqrt{225}$

A 15

B 25

C 5

D 112.5

E 125

6 What is $5^2 \times 3^2$?

A 15

B 60

C 225

D 75

E 90

7 Work out $(-5)^3$

A 15

B -15

C 125

D -125

E -75

8 What is $\sqrt{169} \times \sqrt{49}$?

A 20

B 218

C 91

D 120

E 8281

6.5 Order of operations

1 Work out 3×4^2

  A 12

  B 49

  C 144

  D 24

  E 48

2 What is $(14 - 5)^2$?

  A 81

  B 171

  C 361

  D 221

  E −81

3 Work out $(18 - 8)^2$

  A 260

  B −100

  C 388

  D 100

  E 676

4 Work out $64 - 8^2$

  A 48

  B 0

  C 80

  D 3136

  E 128

5 What is $72 \div 6^2$?

  A 24

  B 144

  C 2

  D 6

  E 9

6 Work out $(24 \div 4)^2$

  A 6

  B 36

  C 72

  D 96

  E 288

7 Work out $5^2 - 2^3$

  A 17

  B 8

  C 4

  D 27

  E 9

8 What is $5^2 - 3^2$?

  A 9

  B 16

  C 4

  D 1

  E 34

9 Work out $\sqrt{36} \times 2$

  A 36

  B 18

  C 12

  D 8

  E $\sqrt{72}$

10 Work out $4 \times \sqrt{9}$

  A 6

  B 12

  C 18

  D $\sqrt{18}$

  E 9

6.7 Prime factors, HCF and LCM

1 Which two numbers are prime factors of 30?

   A 5 and 6

   B 2 and 6

   C 1 and 2

   D 3 and 10

   E 2 and 3

2 Work out the prime factors of 28

   A 2 and 14

   B 1 and 2

   C 2 and 7

   D 7 and 14

   E 1 and 28

3 What is 180 as a product of its prime factors?

   A $2 \times 3 \times 5$

   B $4 \times 9 \times 5$

   C $2^2 \times 3^2 \times 5^2$

   D $2^2 \times 3^2 \times 5$

   E $2 \times 3^2 \times 5^2$

4 What is the HCF of 8 and 12?

   A 6

   B 4

   C 96

   D 2

   E 12

5 What is the LCM of 9 and 15?

   A 3

   B 45

   C 135

   D 15

   E 90

6 Work out the LCM of 20 and 36

   A 180

   B 4

   C 720

   D 2

   E 360

7 What is the HCF of 30 and 70?

   A 2

   B 5

   C 10

   D 210

   E 700

8 What is the LCM of 18 and 12?

   A 6

   B 3

   C 2

   D 36

   E 72

9 Work out the LCM of 48 and 72

   A 24

   B 12

   C 432

   D 8

   E 144

10 Work out the HCF of 35 and 55

   A 11

   B 5

   C 385

   D 7

   E 45

7 Angles (1)

7.1 Triangles

1

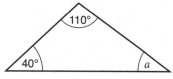

The size of angle a is

A 30°

B 35°

C 40°

D 70°

E 150°

2

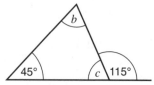

The sizes of angles b and c are

A $b = 65°, c = 70°$

B $b = 90°, c = 45°$

C $b = 70°, c = 65°$

D $b = 115°, c = 20°$

E $b = 115°, c = 65°$

3

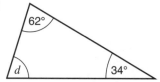

What is the size of angle d?

A 28°

B 34°

C 62°

D 84°

E 96°

4

Here are three statements about the angles a, b and c.

(i) $a + b = 135$
(ii) $c = 45$
(iii) $a + c = 135$

A **(i)** and **(ii)** are true

B **(i)**, **(ii)** and **(iii)** are true

C **(ii)** and **(iii)** are true

D only **(ii)** is true

E only **(i)** is true

5

What is the size of angle x?

A 74°

B 64°

C 36°

D 26°

E 16°

6

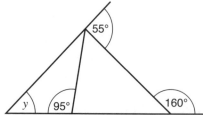

What is the size of angle y?

A 55°

B 45°

C 35°

D 30°

E 25°

7

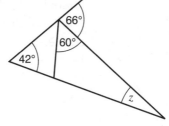

What is the size of angle z?

A 60°

B 24°

C 66°

D 18°

E 30°

8

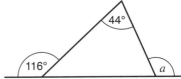

What is the size of angle a?

A 44°

B 108°

C 112°

D 118°

E 136°

9

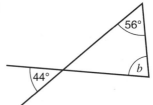

What is the size of angle b?

A 12°

B 44°

C 46°

D 56°

E 80°

10

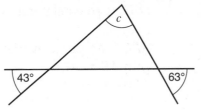

What is the size of angle c?

A 20°

B 43°

C 63°

D 74°

E 106°

7.2 Equilateral triangles and isosceles triangles

1 Look at this diagram and read the two statements about angle a.

(i) Angle a must be greater than 45°

(ii) Angle a must be less than 90°

Which one of the following is true?

A both **(i)** and **(ii)** must be true

B only **(i)** must be true

C only **(ii)** must be true

D neither **(i)** nor **(ii)** is true

E both **(i)** and **(ii)** may be true.

2

DBC is an equilateral triangle.
ABC is an isosceles triangle with *AB* = *AC*.
Angle *A* = 24°

What is the size of angle *ABD*?

A 12°

B 18°

C 24°

D 36°

E 78°

3

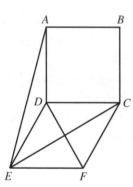

ABCD is a square.
CDF and *DEF* are equilateral triangles.

What is the size of angle *AEC*?

A 15°

B 22$\frac{1}{2}$°

C 30°

D 45°

E 60°

4

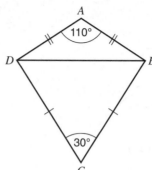

Triangles *ADB* and *CDB* are isosceles.
Angle *A* = 110° and angle *C* = 30°

What is the size of angle *ADC*?

A 70°

B 80°

C 90°

D 110°

E 140°

5

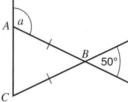

Triangle *ABC* is isosceles.

What is the size of angle *a*?

A 130°

B 115°

C 100°

D 60°

E 50°

6

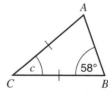

Triangle *ABC* is isosceles.

What is the size of angle *c*?

A 32°

B 58°

C 61°

D 64°

E 122°

7

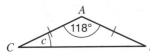

Triangle *ABC* is isosceles.

What is the size of angle *c*?

A 62°

B 31°

C 28°

D 26°

E 14°

8

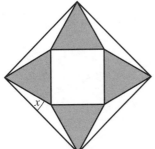

The diagram shows a square surrounded by shaded equilateral triangles.

What is the size of the angle marked *x*?

A 10°

B 20°

C 15°

D 25°

E 30°

9

The diagram is true

A for any value of *x* less than 90°

B only for *x* = 60°

C only for *x* = 30°

D only for *x* = 45°

E only for *x* = 30°, 45° or 60°

10

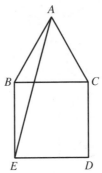

ABC is an equilateral triangle.
BCDE is a square.

What is the size of angle *AED*?

A 45°

B 60°

C 75°

D 30°

E 15°

7.5 Bearings

1 The bearing of *X* from *Y* is 136°.
What is the bearing of *Y* from *X*?

A 046°

B 044°

C 224°

D 226°

E 316°

2 The bearing of *P* from *Q* is 224°.
What is the bearing of *Q* from *P*?

A 044°

B 134°

C 136°

D 314°

E 404°

3

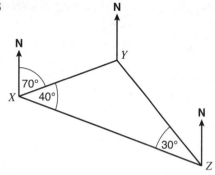

What is the bearing of Z from Y?

A 040°

B 110°

C 140°

D 290°

E 320°

4

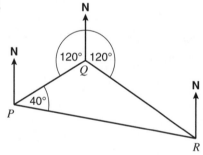

What is the bearing of P from R?

A 080°

B 100°

C 120°

D 260°

E 280°

5

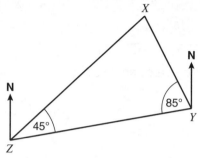

The diagram shows the position of three triangulation points X, Y and Z.
The bearing of X from Y is 345°
What is the bearing of Z from X?

A 035°

B 080°

C 215°

D 225°

E 260°

6

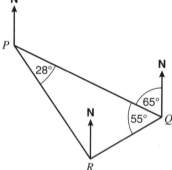

What is the bearing of Q from R?

A 060°

B 097°

C 120°

D 240°

E 300°

7 An aeroplane flies on a bearing of 073°.
It then turns anticlockwise 27°.
What is the new bearing for the aeroplane's flight?

A 280°

B 226°

C 100°

D 056°

E 046°

8 A boat sails on a bearing of 320° before turning 58° clockwise.
What is its new bearing?

A 208°

B 018°

C 272°

D 092°

E 262°

9 X is due East of Y.
The bearing of Z from X is 025°
The bearing of Z from Y is 065°
Which diagram represents this information?

A
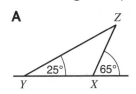

B
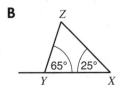

C
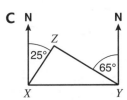

D
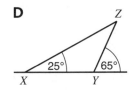

E
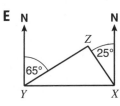

10 P is due North of Q.
The bearing of R from Q is 070°.
What is the bearing of P from R?

A Between 250° and 360°

B Between 000° and 180°

C Between 180° and 270°

D Between 270° and 360°

E Between 000° and 070°

11 Q is due West of P.
The bearing of Q from R is 040°.
$PQ = QR$.
What is the bearing of R from P?

A 065°

B 115°

C 205°

D 230°

E 245°

12 Petr sails from P to Q and then from Q to R.

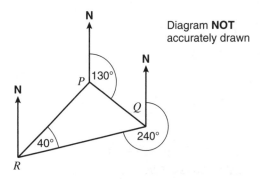

Diagram **NOT** accurately drawn

On what bearing must Petr sail to get back to P?

A 60°

B 40°

C 20°

D 70°

E 50°

8 Expressions and sequences

8.1 Expressions and collecting like terms

1 Jenny has c CDs
She gives 5 CDs to Beryl.

Which of the following is an expression, in terms of c, for the number of CDs Jenny has left?

A $c + 5$

B $5c$

C $\dfrac{c}{5}$

D $cd - 5$

E $c - 5$

2 A bus has p passengers on board when it arrives at a bus stop. 10 passengers get off and 14 passengers get on.

Which of the following is an expression, in terms of p, for the number of passengers on the bus when it leaves the bus stop?

A $p + 4$

B $p - 4$

C $p - 10$

D $p + 14$

E $p + 24$

3 Sweets cost 9 pence each.
Rachael buys s sweets.

Which of the following is an expression, in terms of s, for the total cost?

A s

B $\dfrac{s}{9}$

C $s + 9$

D $\dfrac{9}{s}$

E $9s$

4 There are p pens in a small box and q pens in a large box.
Seamus has 3 small boxes of pens and 2 large boxes of pens.

Which of the following is an expression for the total number of pens Shamus has?

A $p + q$

B $3(p + q)$

C $3p + 2q$

D $3p - 2q$

E $2p + 3q$

5 Simplify $5x - x$

A 5

B $4x$

C 4

D $6x$

E $5x$

6 Simplify $5x - 5$

A x

B $4x$

C 5

D $5x - 5$

E $5x$

7 Simplify $5a + 3b + 3a + 5b$

A $8a + 8b$

B $2a + 2b$

C $8a + 2b$

D $2a + 8b$

E $8a - 2b$

8 Simplify $3x + 4y + 5x - 6y$

A $8x + 10y$

B $8x - 2y$

C $-2x - 2y$

D $8x + 2y$

E $6xy$

9 Wheelbarrows need 1 wheel
Bicycles need 2 wheels
Tricycles need 3 wheels
Quad-bikes need 4 wheels

Which of the following expressions gives the number of wheels that will be needed by w wheelbarrows, t tricycles and q quad-bikes?

A $w + 2t + 4q$

B $12qtw$

C $w + 3t + 4q$

D $w + 2b + 3t + 4q$

E $8wtq$

10 Tim has m marbles.
He bought 20 more and gave 5 away.

Which of the following is an expression, in terms of m, for the number of marbles he has left?

A $m - 15$

B $-15m$

C $m + 15$

D $m + 25$

E $20m - 5$

11 Simplify $3x + 2y - 5x - y$

A $2x + y$

B $-2x + 2$

C $-2xy$

D $-2x + y$

E $2xy$

12 Simplify $5p - 4s - 3p - 2s$

A $2p + 6s$

B $2p - 6s$

C $-4ps$

D $4ps$

E $2p - 2s$

13 Simplify $6a - 7b + 2c - 5a - 3b - c$

A $a - 4b + c$

B $a - 14b + 2$

C $a - 10b + c$

D $a + 4b + c$

E $a + 10b + c$

14 Here is an isosceles triangle

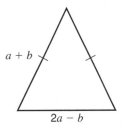

Which of the following is an expression, in terms of a and b, for the perimeter of the triangle?

A $3a$

B $3a + b$

C $4a$

D $4a + 3b$

E $4a + b$

8.2 Working with numbers and letters and using index notation

1 Simplify $2x \times 4y$

  A $6xy$

  B $8xy$

  C $2xy$

  D $24xy$

  E $8x + y$

2 Simplify $5 \times 2k$

  A $7k$

  B $10k$

  C $52k$

  D $5k^2$

  E $25k$

3 Simplify $5 \times p^2$

  A $5p^2$

  B $10p$

  C $25p$

  D $10p^2$

  E $25p^2$

4 What is $5x \times 2x$ in its simplest form?

  A $52x^2$

  B $7xx$

  C $25x^2$

  D $3x^2$

  E $10x^2$

5 Here is a rectangle

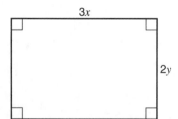

3x

2y

Which of the following is an expression, in terms of x and y, for the area of the rectangle?

  A $5xy$

  B $6x + 4y$

  C $3x + 2y$

  D $6xy$

  E $32xy$

6 Simplify $6 \times 4p \times 2q$

  A $24(p + q)$

  B $12pq$

  C $48pq$

  D $24pq$

  E $36pq$

7 Simplify $6p^2 + 6p - 5p^2 - 6p$

  A $11p^2$

  B $p^2 + 12p$

  C $11p^2 + 12p$

  D p^2

  E $12p$

8.4 Sequences

1 Here are the first five terms of an arithmetic sequence.

    12   19   26   33   40

Which of the following is an expression for the nth term of this sequence?

  A $7n + 12$

  B $7n + 5$

  C $n + 7$

  D $7n$

  E $n + 5$

2 Here are the first five terms of an arithmetic sequence.

    2   5   8   11   14

Which of the following is an expression for the nth term of this sequence?

A $3n + 2$

B $3n - 1$

C $n + 3$

D $3n$

E $n - 1$

3 Here is a pattern made from sticks.

Pattern 1   Pattern 2   Pattern 3

Which of the following is an expression, in terms of n, for the number of sticks in pattern n?

A $3n$

B $2n$

C $n + 2$

D $2n + 1$

E $n + 3$

4 Here is a pattern made from sticks.

Pattern 1   Pattern 2   Pattern 3

Which of the following is an expression, in terms of n, for the number of sticks in pattern n?

A $4n$

B $3n$

C $3n + 1$

D $n + 3$

E $n + 4$

5 Here is a table showing the terms in a number pattern.

Term number	1	2	3	4	5
Term	5	9	13	17	21

Which of the following is an expression, in terms of n, for the nth term of this number pattern?

A $4n$

B $5n$

C $n + 4$

D $n + 5$

E $4n + 1$

6 Here is a table showing the terms in a number pattern.

Term number	1	2	3	4	5
Term	2	7	12	17	22

Which of the following is an expression, in terms of n, for the nth term of this number pattern?

A $2n$

B $5n$

C $n + 5$

D $5n - 3$

E $5n + 2$

7 The nth term of a sequence is given by $2n - 3$
What is the 10th term of this sequence?

A 23

B 14

C 17

D 203

E 197

8 The nth term of a sequence is given by $3n - 2$

What is the 20th term of this sequence?

A 58

B 62

C 88

D 598

E 602

9 The nth term of a sequence is given by $5n + 3$

What is the 10th term of this sequence?

A 503

B 47

C 53

D 497

E 8

10 Here are the first five terms of an arithmetic sequence.

    2   7   12   17   22

Which of the following is an expression for the nth term of this sequence?

A $5n + 2$

B $n + 1$

C $5n - 3$

D $5n$

E $n - 3$

11 Here are the first five terms of an arithmetic sequence.

    2   4   8   16   32

Which of the following is the 10th term of this sequence?

A 512

B 1024

C 246

D 2048

E 112

12 Here are the first five terms of an arithmetic sequence.

    1   3   6   10   15

Which of the following is the 10th term of this sequence?

A 55

B 36

C 78

D 11

E 66

13 If n is a whole number, what type of whole number is $(2n + 3)$?

A Even

B Odd

C Square

D Triangular

E Prime

14 Here are the first five terms of an arithmetic sequence.

    2   7   12   17   22

Which of the following numbers is a member of this sequence?

A 500

B 501

C 502

D 503

E 504

15 Here are the first five terms of an arithmetic sequence.

3 7 11 15 19

Which of the following numbers is **not** a member of this sequence?

A 399

B 199

C 99

D 449

E 639

16 Here are the first five terms of an arithmetic sequence.

100 95 90 85 80

Which of the following is an expression for the nth term of this sequence?

A $5n + 100$

B $n - 5$

C $-5n$

D $100 - 5n$

E $105 - 5n$

17 Here are the first five terms of an arithmetic sequence.

85 77 69 61 53

Which of the following is an expression, in terms of n, for the nth term of this sequence?

A $8n + 5$

B $n - 8$

C $n + 8$

D $93 - 8n$

E $85 - 8n$

18 Here are the first five terms of an arithmetic sequence.

20 15 10 5 0

Which of the following is the 20th term of this sequence?

A -75

B -70

C -80

D -20

E 100

19 Here are the first five terms of an arithmetic sequence.

99 90 81 72 63

Which of the following is the 100th term of this sequence?

A -900

B -801

C 18

D -810

E -792

20 The nth term of a sequence is $100 - 7n$. Which of the following is **not** a term in the sequence?

A 30

B 65

C 44

D 64

E 9

9 Measure

9.1 Compound measures – speed and density

1 A car travels for $2\frac{1}{2}$ hours at a steady speed of 100 km/h. How far does the car travel?

   A 40 km

   B 250 km

   C 25 km

   D 125 km

   E 140 km

2 The density of gold is 13.2 g/cm³. What is the mass of a bar of gold of volume 300 cm³?

   A 0.044 g

   B 16.2 g

   C 396 g

   D 3960 g

   E 44 g

3 Tina drives 300 miles in $2\frac{1}{2}$ hours. What is her average speed?

   A 60 mph

   B 12 mph

   C 25 mph

   D 30 mph

   E 120 mph

4 The density of mercury is 14.2 g/cm³. What is the volume of 20 g of mercury?

   A 140 cm³

   B 284 cm³

   C 1.4 cm³

   D 14 cm³

   E 2.8 cm³

5 An iron bar has a volume of 12 cm³, and a mass of 96 g. What is the density of iron?

   A 1152 g/cm³

   B 108 g/cm³

   C 8 g/cm³

   D 84 g/cm³

   E 80 g/cm³

6 A train has an average speed of 140 km/h. How far does it travel in $3\frac{1}{2}$ hours?

   A 420 km

   B 490 km

   C 40 km

   D 70 km

   E 350 km

7 The density of silver is 10.5 g/cm³. What is the mass of 3 cm³ of silver?

   A 3.5 g

   B 13.5 g

   C 7.5 g

   D 30 g

   E 31.5 g

8 A car travels 210 miles on a tank of 15 litres of fuel. What is the fuel economy of the car, in miles per litre?

   A 315 miles/l

   B 225 miles/l

   C 7 miles/l

   D 14 miles/l

   E 105 miles/l

9 Zinc has a density of 7 g/cm³. What is the volume of zinc that has a mass of 140 g?

  A 20 cm³

  B 980 cm³

  C 200 cm³

  D 98 cm³

  E 133 cm³

10 How many minutes will it take Sandeep to walk $2\frac{1}{2}$ miles at a steady speed of 3 miles per hour?

  A 75 minutes

  B 180 minutes

  C 50 minutes

  D 25 minutes

  E 30 minutes

11 A car travels 96 kilometres on 12 litres of petrol. What is the fuel economy, in kilometres per litre?

  A 1152 km/l

  B 8 km/l

  C 15 km/l

  D 110 km/l

  E 36 km/l

12 Water is flowing at the rate of 0.05 litres per second. What is the flow in litres per hour?

  A 1200 l/h

  B 60 l/h

  C 5 l/h

  D 180 l/h

  E 600 l/h

13 2.5 cm³ of a substance has a mass of 10 grams. What is its density?

  A 25 g/cm³

  B 5 g/cm³

  C 0.25 g/cm³

  D 40 g/cm³

  E 4 g/cm³

14 What is the flow, in litres per hour, if 250 litres flows in 12 minutes?

  A 1250 l/h

  B 20 l/h

  C 3000 l/h

  D 720 l/h

  E 15 000 l/h

15 Martin travels for $2\frac{1}{2}$ hours at a steady speed of 64 miles per hour. How far did he travel in this time?

  A 128 miles

  B 66 miles

  C 160 miles

  D 25.6 miles

  E 96 miles

16 Tin has a density of 7 g/cm³. What is the mass of 70 cm³ of tin?

  A 10 g

  B 4900 g

  C 100 g

  D 49 g

  E 490 g

9.2 Converting between metric and imperial units

1 Darren drives his car 45 miles on a Spanish road. How far is this in kilometres?

A 72 km

B 67 km

C 9 km

D 36 km

E 60 km

2 What is 15 centimetres in inches?

A 7.5 in

B 6 in

C 5 in

D 10 in

E 8 in

3 16 litres of water is put into 1-pint bottles. How many bottles are needed?

A 8

B 10

C 24

D 28

E 30

4 A coach travels a distance of 60 kilometres. What is this in miles?

A 12 miles

B 37.5 miles

C 7.5 miles

D 40 miles

E 35 miles

5 What is 34.1 pounds in kilograms?

A 75 kg

B 17 kg

C 15.5 kg

D 68.2 kg

E 17.5 kg

6 What is 36 inches in centimetres?

A 90 cm

B 14.4 cm

C 18 cm

D 72 cm

E 75 cm

7 A room has a height of 8 feet. What is the height in centimetres?

A 200 cm

B 160 cm

C 48 cm

D 300 cm

E 240 cm

8 A boy's weight is 50 kilograms. What is this in pounds?

A 100 lb

B 110 lb

C 150 lb

D 80 lb

E 90 lb

9 What is 12.5 centimetres in inches?

A 150 in

B 31.25 in

C 20 in

D 5 in

E 2.5 in

10 $3\frac{1}{2}$ gallons of water is put into 1-litre containers. How many containers are needed?

A 7

B 20

C 16

D 12

E 14

11 What is 44 km in miles?

A $5\frac{1}{2}$ miles

B 220 miles

C 70.4 miles

D $27\frac{1}{2}$ miles

E 33 miles

12 The distance between two French towns is 35 miles. What is this distance in kilometres?

A 7 km

B 21.8 km

C 175 km

D 48 km

E 56 km

13 What is 15.75 pints in litres?

A 9 litres

B 12 litres

C 18 litres

D 10 litres

E 7 litres

14 What is 10 miles in kilometres?

A 5 km

B 12 km

C 14 km

D 18 km

E 16 km

15 A piece of wood is 12 inches long. What is its length in centimetres?

A 25 cm

B 24 cm

C 18 cm

D 36 cm

E 30 cm

16 What is 20 kilograms in pounds?

A 10 lb

B 9 lb

C 44 lb

D 40 lb

E 30 lb

17 The fuel tank in Gerri's car holds 12 gallons. When her car travels 21 miles it uses 3 litres of fuel.
How far does Gerri travel if she uses 12 gallons of fuel?

A 378 miles

B 84 miles

C 420 miles

D 540 miles

E 756 miles

10 Decimals and fractions

10.1 Fractions revision

1 If $\frac{24}{30} = \frac{y}{80}$, what is the value of y?

  A   56

  B   60

  C   64

  D   65

  E   72

2 If $\frac{32}{40} = \frac{x}{215}$, what is the value of x?

  A   192

  B   176

  C   172

  D   170

  E   160

3 Which of the following has the same value as $\frac{128}{160}$?

  A $\frac{3}{4}$

  B $\frac{4}{5}$

  C $\frac{5}{6}$

  D $\frac{5}{8}$

  E $\frac{18}{20}$

4 If the fractions $\frac{3}{5}, \frac{8}{15}, \frac{17}{30}$ are written in order of size, starting with the smallest, the order is

  A $\frac{3}{5}, \frac{8}{15}, \frac{17}{30}$

  B $\frac{8}{15}, \frac{3}{5}, \frac{17}{30}$

  C $\frac{17}{30}, \frac{8}{15}, \frac{3}{5}$

  D $\frac{17}{30}, \frac{3}{5}, \frac{8}{15}$

  E $\frac{8}{15}, \frac{17}{30}, \frac{3}{5}$

5 Which of the following has the same value as $3\frac{7}{9}$?

  A $\frac{10}{9}$

  B $\frac{21}{9}$

  C $\frac{34}{9}$

  D $\frac{37}{9}$

  E $\frac{66}{9}$

6 If $\frac{18}{x} = \frac{27}{36}$, what is the value of x?

  A   21

  B   24

  C   27

  D   30

  E   54

7 If $\frac{70}{y} = \frac{2}{3}$, what is the value of y?

  A   210

  B   140

  C   120

  D   105

  E   72

8 Which of the following has the same value as $2\frac{1}{3}$?

  A $\frac{5}{3}$

  B $\frac{7}{3}$

  C $\frac{8}{3}$

  D $\frac{12}{3}$

  E $\frac{21}{3}$

9 Which of the following has the same value as $4\frac{3}{5}$?

A $\frac{17}{5}$

B $\frac{19}{5}$

C $\frac{23}{5}$

D $\frac{34}{5}$

E $\frac{43}{5}$

10 If the fractions $\frac{5}{6}, \frac{19}{24}, \frac{24}{30}$ are written in order of size, starting with the smallest, the order is

A $\frac{19}{24}, \frac{24}{30}, \frac{5}{6}$

B $\frac{5}{6}, \frac{19}{24}, \frac{24}{30}$

C $\frac{24}{30}, \frac{19}{24}, \frac{5}{6}$

D $\frac{19}{24}, \frac{5}{6}, \frac{24}{30}$

E $\frac{24}{30}, \frac{5}{6}, \frac{19}{24}$

11 If the fractions $\frac{16}{20}, \frac{69}{85}, \frac{63}{80}$ are written in order of size, starting with the smallest, the order is

A $\frac{63}{80}, \frac{16}{20}, \frac{69}{85}$

B $\frac{63}{80}, \frac{69}{85}, \frac{16}{20}$

C $\frac{69}{85}, \frac{63}{80}, \frac{16}{20}$

D $\frac{16}{20}, \frac{63}{80}, \frac{69}{85}$

E $\frac{16}{20}, \frac{69}{85}, \frac{63}{80}$

12 Which of the following fractions is not equal to $\frac{3}{5}$?

A $\frac{9}{15}$

B $\frac{18}{25}$

C $\frac{21}{35}$

D $\frac{30}{50}$

E $\frac{60}{100}$

13 Which of the following fractions is bigger than $\frac{7}{8}$?

A $\frac{13}{16}$

B $\frac{20}{24}$

C $\frac{36}{40}$

D $\frac{41}{48}$

E $\frac{69}{80}$

14 Which of the following fractions is smaller than $\frac{5}{7}$?

A $\frac{61}{84}$

B $\frac{21}{28}$

C $\frac{36}{49}$

D $\frac{51}{70}$

E $\frac{31}{56}$

15 When written in its simplest form, $\frac{24}{60}$ is

A $\frac{2}{5}$

B $\frac{4}{10}$

C $\frac{6}{15}$

D $\frac{8}{20}$

E $\frac{12}{30}$

16 Which of the following fractions is smaller than $\frac{3}{8}$?

A $\frac{7}{16}$

B $\frac{8}{24}$

C $\frac{16}{40}$

D $\frac{19}{48}$

E $\frac{27}{72}$

17 Which of the following fractions is larger than $\frac{8}{15}$?

- **A** $\frac{40}{76}$
- **B** $\frac{31}{60}$
- **C** $\frac{24}{45}$
- **D** $\frac{16}{30}$
- **E** $\frac{16}{29}$

18 Which of the following fractions is not equal to $\frac{162}{270}$?

- **A** $\frac{81}{135}$
- **B** $\frac{54}{90}$
- **C** $\frac{19}{30}$
- **D** $\frac{9}{15}$
- **E** $\frac{3}{5}$

19 Which of the following fractions is not equal to $\frac{54}{120}$?

- **A** $\frac{9}{20}$
- **B** $\frac{17}{40}$
- **C** $\frac{18}{40}$
- **D** $\frac{27}{60}$
- **E** $\frac{81}{180}$

20 Which of the following fractions has the same value as $\frac{84}{192}$?

- **A** $\frac{7}{15}$
- **B** $\frac{14}{31}$
- **C** $\frac{28}{63}$
- **D** $\frac{42}{94}$
- **E** $\frac{126}{288}$

10.2 Arithmetic of decimals

1 Work out $15.1 - 2.37$

- **A** 12.64
- **B** 12.73
- **C** 13.36
- **D** 13.64
- **E** 13.73

2 Work out $37.3 - 8.59$

- **A** 29.29
- **B** 29.71
- **C** 29.44
- **D** 28.71
- **E** 28.44

3 Work out 36.21×0.03

- **A** 0.0010863
- **B** 0.010863
- **C** 0.10863
- **D** 1.0863
- **E** 10.863

4 Work out 0.00213×1000

- **A** 213
- **B** 21.3
- **C** 2.13
- **D** 0.213
- **E** 0.0213

5 Work out 2.1×0.017

- **A** 0.00357
- **B** 0.0168
- **C** 0.0357
- **D** 0.168
- **E** 0.357

6 When the numbers 0.07806, 0.07796, 0.07087, 0.0781 and 0.08 are written in order of size, starting with the smallest, the order is

   A   0.07087, 0.07796, 0.07806, 0.0781, 0.08

   B   0.07087, 0.07806, 0.0781, 0.07796, 0.08

   C   0.08, 0.0781, 0.07087, 0.07796, 0.07806

   D   0.0781, 0.07087, 0.07796, 0.07806, 0.08

   E   0.07087, 0.07796, 0.0781, 0.07806, 0.08

7 When 5.03 is multiplied by 0.056 the number of decimal places in the answer is

   A   2

   B   3

   C   4

   D   5

   E   6

8 Work out $6.37 \div 0.01$

   A   0.0637

   B   0.637

   C   63.7

   D   637

   E   6370

9 Work out $0.036 \div 0.02$

   A   180

   B   18

   C   1.8

   D   0.18

   E   0.018

10 Work out $0.28 \div 0.007$

   A   400

   B   40

   C   4

   D   0.4

   E   0.04

11 When 37 is divided by 8 the number of decimal places in the answer is

   A   1

   B   2

   C   3

   D   4

   E   5

12 Work out 13.1×0.4

   A   0.00524

   B   0.0524

   C   0.524

   D   5.24

   E   52.4

13 What is the value of 0.32×5.6 to two significant figures?

   A   1.79

   B   1.8

   C   2.8

   D   17.92

   E   18

14 Work out $12.15 \div 0.3$

   A   0.405

   B   4.05

   C   4.5

   D   40.5

   E   45

15 When 43 is divided by 4, the number of significant figures in the answer is

   A   4

   B   3

   C   2

   D   1

   E   0

16 When the numbers 1.32, 1.4, 1.327 and 1.3168 are written in order of size, starting with the smallest, the order is

A   1.4, 1.32, 1.327, 1.3168

B   1.4, 1.327, 1.32, 1.3168

C   1.3168, 1.32, 1.327, 1.4

D   1.32, 1.327, 1.3168, 1.4

E   1.3168, 1.327, 1.32, 1.4

10.6 Rounding to significant figures

1 The number of significant figures in 0.03009 is

A   2

B   3

C   4

D   5

E   6

2 The number of significant figures in 503.06 is

A   1

B   2

C   3

D   4

E   5

3 When written to two significant figures, 20.257 is

A   20

B   20.2

C   20.25

D   20.26

E   20.3

4 When written to one significant figure, 7.092 is

A   7.1

B   7.09

C   7.000

D   7.0

E   7

5 When written to three significant figures 53 456 is

A   535

B   534

C   53 500

D   53 400

E   53 600

6 When written to three significant figures 0.000 053 456 is

A   0.535

B   535

C   0.000 535 00

D   0.000 534 00

E   0.000 535

7 The number of significant figures in 0.000 450 is

A   2

B   3

C   5

D   6

E   7

11 Expanding brackets and factorising

11.1 Expanding brackets

1 Expand $2(b + 3)$

  A $2b + 3$

  B $2b - 3$

  C $b + 6$

  D $2b + 6$

  E $12b$

2 Expand $3(2c + 5)$

  A $6c + 5$

  B $2c + 15$

  C $6c + 15$

  D $21c$

  E $5c + 15$

3 Expand $5(g - 2)$

  A $10g - 10$

  B $5g + 10$

  C $5g - 2$

  D $-5g$

  E $5g - 10$

4 Expand $3(4p - 5)$

  A $12p - 15$

  B $-3p$

  C $4p - 15$

  D $12p - 5$

  E $12p + 15$

5 Expand $4(2x + 3y)$

  A $8x + 3y$

  B $8x + 12y$

  C $20xy$

  D $2x + 12y$

  E $6x + 12y$

6 Expand $2(7a - 3b)$

  A $8ab$

  B $14a - 3b$

  C $14a - 6b$

  D $20ab$

  E $7a - 6b$

7 Expand $5(3k + 2m + 3)$

  A $40km$

  B $15k + 10m + 3$

  C $15k + 25m$

  D $15k + 10m + 15$

  E $25km + 15$

8 Expand $x(x - 1)$

  A $x^2 - 1$

  B $x^2 - x$

  C $2x - 1$

  D x

  E $x^2 + x$

9 Expand $2x(3x - 5y)$

  A $5x^2 - 10xy$

  B $6x^2 - 5y$

  C $6x - 10xy$

  D $5x^2 - 7xy$

  E $6x^2 - 10xy$

10 Expand $-(n - 2)$

  A $-n + 2$

  B $-n - 2$

  C $n + 2$

  D $n - 2$

  E $-2n$

11 Expand and simplify $3(p + 4) + 2(p - 3)$

  A $5p + 18$

  B $5p + 6$

  C $5p + 2$

  D $p + 6$

  E $11p$

12 Expand and simplify $6(2x - 3) - 2(4x - 5)$

  A $20x - 28$

  B $4x - 28$

  C $2x + 1$

  D $4x - 8$

  E $4x + 8$

13 Expand and simplify $t(2t - 3) - 3t(2t - 5)$

  A $12t - 7t^2$

  B $18t - 4t^2$

  C $12t - 4t^2$

  D $12t - 3t^2$

  E $-18t - 4t^2$

11.2 Factorising by taking out common factors

1 Factorise $5x + 10$

  A $5(x + 10)$

  B 5

  C $5(x - 2)$

  D $10(x + 1)$

  E $5(x + 2)$

2 Factorise $12p - 12$

  A $12(p - 1)$

  B $12(p + 1)$

  C $12p$

  D p

  E $6(2p - 1)$

3 Factorise $3y - 12x$

  A 3

  B $3(y + 4x)$

  C $3(y - 4x)$

  D $-4xy$

  E $3(y - 4)$

4 Factorise $12x - 8y$

  A $2(x - 4y)$

  B $4(x - y)$

  C $3x - 2y$

  D $4(3x - 2y)$

  E 4

5 Factorise $gh - hj$

  A $g(h - j)$

  B $h(g - j)$

  C $j(g - h)$

  D $h(1 - j)$

  E $h(g - 1)$

6 Factorise $4y^2 - y$

  A $y(4y - 1)$

  B $y(4y - y)$

  C y

  D $y(y - 1)$

  E $(4y - 1)$

7 Factorise completely $6xy + 9y$

  A $y(6x + 9)$

  B $3(2xy + 3y)$

  C $3y$

  D $2x + 3y$

  E $3y(2x + 3)$

8 Factorise completely $6abc - bc$

  A $b(6ac - c)$

  B $c(6ab - b)$

  C $bc(6a - bc)$

  D $bc(6a - 1)$

  E $6a(bc - bc)$

9 Factorise completely $x^2y - xy^2$

  A $x(xy - y^2)$

  B $xy(x - y)$

  C $y(x^2 - xy)$

  D $x^2y^2(x - y)$

  E xy

10 Factorise completely $9t^2 + 3t$

  A $t(9t + 3)$

  B $3(3t^2 + t)$

  C $3t(3t + 0)$

  D $3t$

  E $3t(3t + 1)$

11 Factorise completely $12x^2y^2z + 18xyz^2$

  A $6xyz(2x + 3z)$

  B $6(2xyz + 3xyz)$

  C $6xyz(2xy + 3z)$

  D $xyz(12xy + 18z)$

  E xyz

12 Factorise completely $16x^2y - 8xy^2$

  A $8xy(2x - y)$

  B $4xy(4x - 2y)$

  C $2xy(8x - 4y)$

  D $xy(16x - 8y)$

  E $8x^2y^2(2x - y)$

11.3 Expanding the product of two brackets

1 Expand and simplify $(x + 3)(x + 4)$

  A $x^2 + 12$

  B $x^2 + 7x$

  C $x^2 + 7x + 12$

  D $x^2 + 19x$

  E $x^2 + 7x + 7$

2 Expand and simplify $(x + 2)(x - 5)$

  A $x^2 - 10$

  B $x^2 + 10$

  C $x^2 + 7x - 10$

  D $x^2 - 3x - 10$

  E $x^2 - 7x - 10$

3 Expand and simplify $(x - 4)(x + 6)$

  A $x^2 + 2x - 24$

  B $x^2 - 24$

  C $x^2 - 10x - 24$

  D $x^2 + 24$

  E $x^2 - 2x - 24$

4 Expand and simplify $(x - 5)(x - 4)$

  A $x^2 - 20$

  B $x^2 + 20$

  C $x^2 + 9x + 20$

  D $x^2 - 9x - 20$

  E $x^2 - 9x + 20$

5 Expand and simplify $(x - 5)(x + 3)$

  A $x^2 + 2x - 15$

  B $x^2 - 2x - 15$

  C $x^2 - 15$

  D $x^2 + 2x + 15$

  E $x^2 - 2x + 15$

6 Expand and simplify $(x + 5)(x - 4)$

  A $x^2 - 9x - 20$

  B $x^2 - 20$

  C $x^2 - x - 20$

  D $x^2 + x - 20$

  E $x^2 + 9x + 20$

7 Expand and simplify $(x + 4)(x - 4)$

  A $x^2 + 16$

  B $x^2 - 16$

  C $x^2 + 8x + 16$

  D $x^2 - 8x - 16$

  E $x^2 + 8x - 16$

8 Expand and simplify $(p + 4)^2$

  A $p^2 + 16$

  B $p^2 - 16$

  C $p^2 + 8p + 16$

  D $p^2 - 8p - 16$

  E $p^2 - 8p + 16$

9 Expand and simplify $(s - 5)^2$

  A $s^2 + 25$

  B $s^2 - 25$

  C $s^2 + 10s + 25$

  D $s^2 + 10s - 25$

  E $s^2 - 10s + 25$

10 Expand and simplify $(c + d)(c - d)$

  A $c^2 + d^2$

  B $c^2 - d^2$

  C $c^2 + 2cd + d^2$

  D $c^2 - 2cd - d^2$

  E $c^2 - 2cd + d^2$

11 Expand and simplify $(p + q)(p + q)$

  A $p^2 + q^2$

  B $p^2 - q^2$

  C $p^2 + 2pq + q^2$

  D $p^2 - 2pq - q^2$

  E $p^2 - 2pq + q^2$

12 Expand and simplify $(2p + 3)(3p + 5)$

  A $6p^2 + 19p + 15$

  B $6p^2 + 15$

  C $5p^2 + 8$

  D $5p^2 + 19p + 15$

  E $6p^2 + p + 15$

13 Expand and simplify $(3y + 5)(4y - 3)$

  A $12y^2 + 11y - 15$

  B $12y^2 - 15$

  C $12y^2 + 15$

  D $12y^2 - 11y - 15$

  E $12y^2 - 11y + 15$

14 Expand and simplify $(2k - 1)(5k - 4)$

   A $10k^2 - 4$

   B $10k^2 + 13k + 4$

   C $10k^2 - 13k + 4$

   D $10k^2 + 4$

   E $10k^2 - 13k - 4$

15 Expand and simplify $(3h - 4)^2$

   A $9h^2 + 16$

   B $9h^2 - 16$

   C $9h^2 + 24h - 16$

   D $9h^2 - 24h - 16$

   E $9h^2 - 24h + 16$

11.4 Factorising by grouping

1 Factorise completely $p(q + 2) + 3(q + 2)$

   A $5(p + q)$

   B $(p + 3)(q + 2)$

   C $3p(q + 2)$

   D $2q(p + 3)$

   E $pq + 5$

2 Factorise completely $g(h - 4) - 5(h - 4)$

   A $g(h - 4)$

   B $(g - 5)(h + 4)$

   C $5g(h - 4)$

   D $4h(g - 5)$

   E $(g - 5)(h - 4)$

3 Factorise completely $cd - ce + fd - fe$

   A $(c + d)(e - f)$

   B $(c + f)(d - e)$

   C $(c - e)(d + f)$

   D $(c - f)(d + e)$

   E $cf(d - e)$

4 Factorise completely $x^2 + bx - xy - by$

   A $xy(b - y)$

   B $xb(b - y)$

   C $(x + b)(y - b)$

   D $(x + b)(x - y)$

   E $(x - b)(x - y)$

5 Factorise completely $3x^2 - 9x + 5xy - 15y$

   A $(3x - 9)(5x - 3)$

   B $xy(3x - 5y)$

   C $(3x + 5y)(x - 3)$

   D $3(x - 3)(y + 5)$

   E $(3x - 5y)(x + 3)$

11.5 Factorising expressions of the form $x^2 + bx + c$

1 Factorise $x^2 + 7x + 12$

   A $(x + 3)(x + 4)$

   B $(x - 3)(x - 4)$

   C $(x + 6)(x + 2)$

   D $(x + 3)(x - 4)$

   E $(x - 3)(x + 4)$

2 Factorise $x^2 - 7x + 12$

   A $(x + 3)(x + 4)$

   B $(x - 3)(x - 4)$

   C $(x - 6)(x - 2)$

   D $(x + 3)(x - 4)$

   E $(x - 3)(x + 4)$

3 Factorise $x^2 + x - 12$

   A $(x + 3)(x + 4)$

   B $(x - 3)(x - 4)$

   C $(x + 6)(x - 2)$

   D $(x + 3)(x - 4)$

   E $(x - 3)(x + 4)$

4 Factorise $x^2 - x - 12$

  A $(x + 3)(x + 4)$

  B $(x - 3)(x - 4)$

  C $(x - 6)(x + 2)$

  D $(x + 3)(x - 4)$

  E $(x - 3)(x + 4)$

5 Factorise $x^2 - 4x - 12$

  A $(x + 3)(x + 4)$

  B $(x - 3)(x - 4)$

  C $(x - 6)(x + 2)$

  D $(x + 3)(x - 4)$

  E $(x - 3)(x + 4)$

6 Factorise $p^2 - 6p + 9$

  A $(p + 3)(p + 3)$

  B $(p - 3)(p - 3)$

  C $(p + 9)(p - 1)$

  D $(p + 3)(p - 3)$

  E $(p - 9)(p + 1)$

7 Factorise $2s^2 + 3s + 1$

  A $(2s + 1)(s + 1)$

  B $(2s - 1)(s - 1)$

  C $(2s + 1)(s - 1)$

  D $(2s - 1)(s + 1)$

  E $(2s + \frac{1}{2})(s + 2)$

8 Factorise $3k^2 - 5k + 2$

  A $(3k + 1)(k + 2)$

  B $(3k - 1)(k - 2)$

  C $(3k - 2)(k - 1)$

  D $(3k + 2)(k + 1)$

  E $(k + 1)(3k - 2)$

9 One of the factors of $3x^2 + 13x - 10$ is $(x + 5)$

What is the other factor?

  A $(3x + 2)$

  B $(3x - 2)$

  C $3(x + 1)$

  D $(x - 2)$

  E $(3x - 5)$

10 One of the factors of $2x^2 - 5x - 12$ is $(x - 4)$

What is the other factor?

  A $(2x + 3)$

  B $(2x - 3)$

  C $2(x + 1)$

  D $(x + 3)$

  E $2(x + 3)$

11 One of the factors of $6x^2 - 5x - 6$ is $(3x + 2)$

What is the other factor?

  A $(2x + 3)$

  B $(2x - 3)$

  C $2(x - 1)$

  D $(3 - 2x)$

  E $2(x - 3)$

12 $2x + 3$ is a factor of

  A $2x^2 + x - 3$

  B $2x^2 - x - 3$

  C $4x^2 + 5x + 1$

  D $4x^2 - 3x + 3$

  E $4x^2 - 15x + 4$

12 Two-dimensional shapes (1)

12.1 Special quadrilaterals

1 What is the special name of this quadrilateral?

- **A** Square
- **B** Rectangle
- **C** Trapezium
- **D** Kite
- **E** Rhombus

2 What is the special name of this quadrilateral?

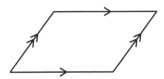

- **A** Parallelogram
- **B** Square
- **C** Trapezium
- **D** Rhombus
- **E** Kite

3 What is the special name of this quadrilateral?

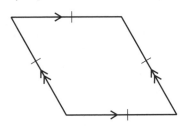

- **A** Rectangle
- **B** Parallelogram
- **C** Rhombus
- **D** Kite
- **E** Square

4 What is the special name of this quadrilateral?

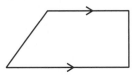

- **A** Square
- **B** Trapezium
- **C** Parallelogram
- **D** Kite
- **E** Square

12.2 Perimeter and area of rectangles

1 What is the area of a rectangle with sides 8 cm and 5 cm?

- **A** 14 cm^2
- **B** 40 cm^2
- **C** 26 cm^2
- **D** 20 cm^2
- **E** 13 cm^2

2 What is the perimeter of a rectangle with sides 8 cm and 5 cm?

- **A** 14 cm
- **B** 40 cm
- **C** 26 cm
- **D** 20 cm
- **E** 13 cm

3 Work out the perimeter of a square of side 6 cm.

 A 24 cm

 B 36 cm

 C 12 cm

 D 18 cm

 E 6 cm

4 Work out the area of a square of side 6 cm.

 A 24 cm^2

 B 36 cm^2

 C 12 cm^2

 D 18 cm^2

 E 6 cm^2

5 A square has an area of 64 cm^2.
What is the length of one side?

 A 32 cm

 B 16 cm

 C 4 cm

 D 8 cm

 E 2 cm

6 The length of a rectangle is 8 cm and its area is 40 cm^2.
What is the width of the rectangle?

 A 320 cm

 B 8 cm

 C 10 cm

 D 6 cm

 E 5 cm

7 A square has an area of 169 cm^2.
What is the length of one side?

 A 84.5 cm

 B 42.5 cm

 C 13 cm

 D 6.5 cm

 E 31 cm

8 A rectangle has length 5 cm and perimeter 22 cm.
What is its width?

 A 110 cm

 B 5 cm

 C 6 cm

 D 4.4 cm

 E 17 cm

9 A rectangle has a width of 7 cm and area of 35 cm^2.
What is its length?

 A 42 cm

 B 245 cm

 C 28 cm

 D 5 cm

 E 21 cm

10 A square has an area of 144 cm^2.
What is the length of one side?

 A 12 cm

 B 36 cm

 C 6 cm

 D 72 cm

 E 18 cm

12.3 Area of a parallelogram

1 The rule to work out the area of a parallelogram with base b and height h is

    A bh

    B $\frac{1}{2}bh$

    C $2bh$

    D h^2

    E b^2

2 What is the area of this parallelogram?

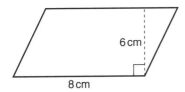

6 cm

8 cm

    A $24\,\text{cm}^2$

    B $48\,\text{cm}^2$

    C $64\,\text{cm}^2$

    D $36\,\text{cm}^2$

    E $12\,\text{cm}^2$

3 What is the area of this parallelogram?

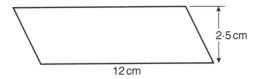

2·5 cm

12 cm

    A $144\,\text{cm}^2$

    B $28\,\text{cm}^2$

    C $30\,\text{cm}^2$

    D $18\,\text{cm}^2$

    E $144\,\text{cm}^2$

4 Work out the area of this parallelogram.

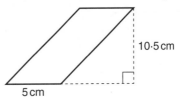

10·5 cm

5 cm

    A $27.5\,\text{cm}^2$

    B $52.5\,\text{cm}^2$

    C $41\,\text{cm}^2$

    D $15.5\,\text{cm}^2$

    E $55\,\text{cm}^2$

5 A parallelogram has a height of 12 cm and parallel sides each 13 cm long.
Work out the area.

    A $50\,\text{cm}^2$

    B $25\,\text{cm}^2$

    C $156\,\text{cm}^2$

    D $78\,\text{cm}^2$

    E $38\,\text{cm}^2$

6 A parallelogram has an area of $80\,\text{cm}^2$ and height of 5 cm.
What is the length of the base?

    A   400 cm

    B   8 cm

    C   85 cm

    D   16 cm

    E   170 cm

7 A parallelogram has a base of 12 cm and an area of $108\,\text{cm}^2$.
Work out the height.

    A   9 cm

    B   120 cm

    C   240 cm

    D   14.5 cm

    E   6 cm

8 Work out the area of this parallelogram.

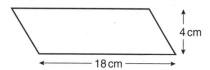

A   22 cm²

B   44 cm²

C   72 cm²

D   36 cm²

E   144 cm²

9 How long is the base of this parallelogram?

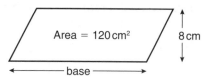

A   1076 cm

B   75 cm

C   12 cm

D   15 cm

E   18 cm

10 Work out the height of this parallelogram.

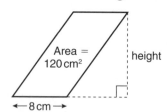

A   16 cm

B   960 cm

C   15 cm

D   30 cm

E   7.5 cm

12.4 Area of a triangle

1 What is the area of this triangle?

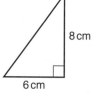

A   48 cm²

B   24 cm²

C   14 cm²

D   7 cm²

E   12 m²

2 Work out the area of this triangle.

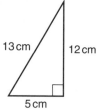

A   30 cm

B   60 cm²

C   30 cm²

D   15 cm²

E   156 m²

3 A triangle has a base of 4 cm and a height of 15 cm.
Work out the area.

A   30 cm²

B   15 cm²

C   60 cm²

D   19 cm²

E   95 cm²

4 What is the area of this triangle?

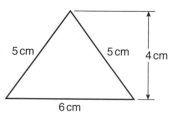

A   30 cm

B   12 cm²

C   15 cm²

D   24 cm²

E   25 cm²

5 Work out the area of this triangle.

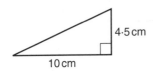

- **A** 14.5 cm²
- **B** 45 cm²
- **C** 7.25 cm²
- **D** 4.5 cm²
- **E** 22.5 cm²

6 A triangle has an area of 30 cm².
The height of the triangle is 6 cm.
Work out the length of the base of the
triangle.

- **A** 24 cm
- **B** 5 cm
- **C** 10 cm
- **D** 36 cm
- **E** 2.5 cm

7 A triangle has an area of 50 cm².
The base of the triangle is 5 cm.
What is the height of the triangle?

- **A** 10 cm
- **B** 20 cm
- **C** 5 cm
- **D** 25 cm
- **E** 45 cm

8 A triangle has a base of 8 cm and height of
2 m. Work out the area of the triangle.

- **A** 8 cm²
- **B** 8 m²
- **C** 800 cm²
- **D** 80 cm²
- **E** 16 000 m²

9 A triangle has a base of 12 cm and an area
of 168 cm².
Work out the height of the triangle.

- **A** 56 cm
- **B** 28 cm
- **C** 13 cm
- **D** 144 cm
- **E** 1008 cm

10 Work out the height of this triangle.

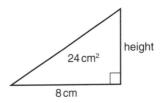

- **A** 3 cm
- **B** 16 cm
- **C** 8 cm
- **D** 12 cm
- **E** 6 cm

12.5 Area of a trapezium

1 Work out the area of this trapezium.

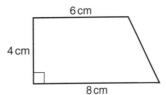

- **A** 56 cm²
- **B** 112 cm²
- **C** 14 cm²
- **D** 28 cm²
- **E** 32 cm²

2 Work out the area of this shape.

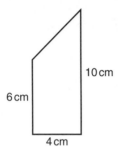

A 32 cm²

B 64 cm²

C 16 cm²

D 24 cm²

E 60 cm²

3 What is the area of this trapezium?

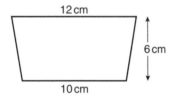

A 112 cm²

B 66 cm²

C 720 cm²

D 60 cm²

E 72 cm²

4 Work out the area of this trapezium.

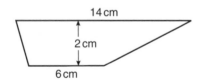

A 40 cm²

B 10 cm²

C 20 cm²

D 12 cm²

E 28 cm²

5 What is the area of this trapezium?

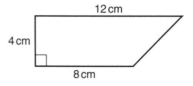

A 20 cm²

B 80 cm²

C 32 cm²

D 48 cm²

E 40 cm²

6 Work out the area of this trapezium.

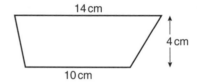

A 24 cm²

B 96 cm²

C 48 cm²

D 40 cm²

E 56 cm²

7 What is the area of this trapezium?

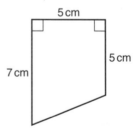

A 15 cm²

B 30 cm²

C 60 cm²

D 25 cm²

E 35 cm²

8 Work out the area of this trapezium.

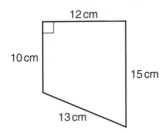

- **A** 300 cm²
- **B** 162.5 cm²
- **C** 150 cm²
- **D** 156.25 cm²
- **E** 75 cm²

9 Work out the area of this trapezium.

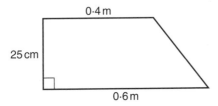

- **A** 6 m²
- **B** 60 cm²
- **C** 1250 cm²
- **D** 12.5 cm²
- **E** 600 cm²

10 Work out the area of this trapezium.

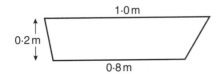

- **A** 0.18 m²
- **B** 1.8 m²
- **C** 18 m²
- **D** 180 m²
- **E** 0.018 m²

12.6 Problems involving areas

1 Work out the area of this shape.

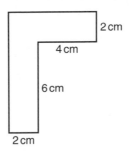

- **A** 20 cm²
- **B** 48 cm²
- **C** 40 cm²
- **D** 28 cm²
- **E** 24 cm²

2 Work out the area of this shape.

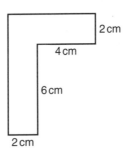

- **A** 14 cm²
- **B** 26 cm²
- **C** 24 cm²
- **D** 28 cm²
- **E** 20 cm²

3 Work out the area of the lawn around the pond.

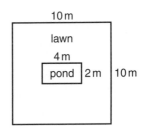

- **A** 12 m²
- **B** 92 m²
- **C** 28 m²
- **D** 48 m²
- **E** 8 m²

4 Work out the area of this shape.

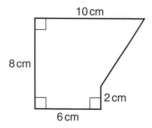

A 72 cm²

B 80 cm²

C 60 cm²

D 66 cm²

E 54 cm²

5 Work out the area of the shaded shape.

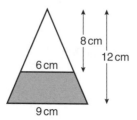

A 30 cm²

B 15 cm²

C 72 cm²

D 54 cm²

E 60 cm²

6 Work out the area of this shape.

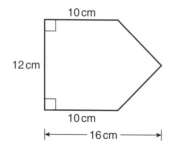

A 192 cm²

B 96 cm²

C 78 cm²

D 156 cm²

E 80 cm²

7 How many 25 cm × 25 cm square tiles do you need to cover 2 m² of floor?

A 16

B 8

C 32

D 24

E 64

8 Work out the area of this trapezium.

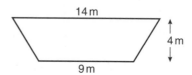

A 96 m²

B 23 m²

C 46 m²

D 126 m²

E 92 m²

9 A rectangle measures 16 cm by 4 cm. A square has the same area. What is the length of the side of the square?

A 32 cm

B 8 cm

C 16 cm

D 12 cm

E 24 cm

10 A square has 12 cm sides. A rectangle has the same area. The length of one side of the rectangle is 8 cm. What is the length of the other side?

A 12 cm

B 18 cm

C 9 cm

D 6 cm

E 15 cm

13 Graphs (1)

13.1 Coordinates and line segments

1 What is the midpoint of the line segment joining $(1, 2)$ to $(5, 12)$?

  A $(3, 5)$

  B $(3, 7)$

  C $(3, 14)$

  D $(4, 10)$

  E $(9, 22)$

2 What is the midpoint of the line segment joining $(3, 7)$ to $(-5, 9)$?

  A $(-1, 8)$

  B $(-1, 11)$

  C $(-2, 16)$

  D $(-4, 8)$

  E $(-8, 2)$

3 What is the midpoint of the line segment joining $(-4, 3)$ to $(-6, -7)$?

  A $(2, 10)$

  B $(-10, -4)$

  C $(-5, -2)$

  D $(-5, -5)$

  E $(-8, -17)$

4 What is the midpoint of the line segment joining (p, q) to (r, s)?

  A $(p + r, q + s)$

  B $(\frac{1}{2}pr, \frac{1}{2}qs)$

  C $(\frac{1}{2}(r - p), \frac{1}{2}(s - q))$

  D $(\frac{1}{2}(p - r), \frac{1}{2}(q - s))$

  E $(\frac{1}{2}(p + r), \frac{1}{2}(q + s))$

5 $(1, 1)$, $(2, 0)$ and $(4, 1)$ are three vertices of a parallelogram.
Which of the following points could complete the parallelogram?
$(5, 0)$, $(3, 2)$, $(-1, 0)$, $(2, 2)$

  A all except $(2, 2)$

  B all except $(5, 0)$

  C all except $(3, 2)$

  D all except $(-1, 0)$

  E all of them

6 $(1, 1)$, $(3, 0)$ and $(4, 1)$ are three vertices of a kite.
What are the coordinates of the fourth vertex?

  A $(0, 0)$

  B $(1, 2)$

  C $(2, 2)$

  D $(3, 2)$

  E $(6, 0)$

7 $M(3, 2)$ is the midpoint of the line segment PQ where P is $(-1, 7)$.
What are the coordinates of Q?

  A $(1, 4\frac{1}{2})$

  B $(2, -2\frac{1}{2})$

  C $(-4, 5)$

  D $(-5, 12)$

  E $(7, -3)$

8 (1, 3) and (3, 1) are two vertices of an isosceles triangle.
Which of the following points does not complete an isosceles triangle?

A (−1, 1)

B (1, 1)

C (2, 2)

D (−5, 3)

E (5, 5)

9 What is the midpoint of the line segment joining (4, 5) to (−8, −7)?

A (−2, 1)

B (−2, −1)

C (−4, −1)

D (−4, −2)

E (−20, −19)

10 What is the midpoint of the line joining (−5, −6) to (−1, −14)?

A (−7, −2)

B (−6, −20)

C (−3, −10)

D (−3, 10)

E (3, −10)

11 The points (1, 3) and (7, 3) are two vertices of an isosceles triangle.
How many of the following points could be the third vertex of the triangle?
(1, 9) (4, 0), (1, −3) (7, −3)(4, −3) (4, $2\frac{1}{2}$)

A 6

B 5

C 4

D 3

E 2

12 The points (1, 1) and (5, 1) are two vertices of a right-angled triangle.
How many of the following points could complete the right-angled triangle?
(1, 4) (3, 4) (3, −2) (5, −2) (2, 3)

A 1

B 2

C 3

D 4

E 5

Use this diagram to answer questions **13–15**.

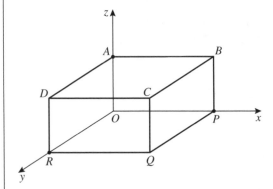

The diagram shows a cuboid $ABCDOPQR$. Points $P(4, 0, 0)$, $A(0, 3, 0)$ and $R(0, 0, 5)$ are identified.

13 What is the midpoint of AB?

A (2, 0, 3)

B (3, 0, 2)

C (0, 2, 3)

D (2, 3, 0)

E (0, 0, 3)

14 What is the midpoint of OQ?

A (5, 4, 0)

B (4, 5, 0)

C (2, $2\frac{1}{2}$, 0)

D (2, 0, $2\frac{1}{2}$)

E (0, $2\frac{1}{2}$, 2)

15 What is the midpoint of RD?

   A $(0, 1\frac{1}{2}, 5)$

   B $(2, 1\frac{1}{2}, 2\frac{1}{2})$

   C $(5, 0, 3)$

   D $(3, 0, 5)$

   E $(2\frac{1}{2}, 0, 1\frac{1}{2})$

16 $P(2, 3, 0)$, $Q(4, 0, 2\frac{1}{2})$ and $R(0, 0, 5)$ are three vertices of parallelogram $PQRS$. What are the coordinates of S?

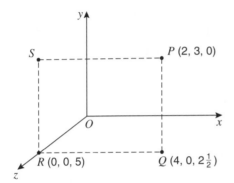

   A $(-2, 3, 2\frac{1}{2},)$

   B $(-2, 2\frac{1}{2}, 3)$

   C $(0, 3, 2\frac{1}{2})$

   D $(2, 3, 5)$

   E $(2, 0, 0)$

17 $PQRS$ is a parallelogram.
Three vertices are $P(-3, -4)$, $Q(-1, -1)$ and $S(3, -1)$.
The fourth coordinate, R, of the parallelogram is in the first quadrant.
What is the coordinate of R?

   A $(4, 1)$

   B $(5, 3)$

   C $(4, 3)$

   D $(5, 2)$

   E $(9, 2)$

18 $(3, 2)$ and $(6, 1)$ is one side of a right-angled triangle.
How many of the following coordinates could be the third vertex?
$(4, 5)$ $(5, -2)$ $(5, 8)$ $(7, 4)$ $(2, -1)$ $(0, -7)$

   A 4

   B 6

   C 5

   D 3

   E 2

19 $(1, 5)$ and $(7, 5)$ are one side of an isosceles triangle. Which of the following points **cannot** be the third reflex?

   A $(4, 3)$

   B $(7, -1)$

   C $(4, 5)$

   D $(1, 11)$

   E $(4, -5)$

14 Estimating and accuracy

14.1 Significant figures

1 How many significant figures are there in 0.030 09?

  A 2

  B 3

  C 4

  D 5

  E 6

2 How many significant figures are there in 503.06?

  A 1

  B 2

  C 3

  D 4

  E 5

3 Which of the following is the value of 20.257 when written to 2 significant figures?

  A 20

  B 20.2

  C 20.3

  D 20.25

  E 20.26

4 Which of the following is the value of 7.092 when written to 1 significant figure?

  A 7

  B 7.0

  C 7.1

  D 7.09

  E 7.000

5 What is the answer to 0.38×5.3 when given to 2 significant figures?

  A 2

  B 2.1

  C 2.01

  D 2.0

  E 2.014

6 What is the answer to $18.3 \div 2.4$ when given to 2 significant figures?

  A 8.0

  B 7.625

  C 7.63

  D 7.62

  E 7.6

7 (i) 140 (ii) 2.63 (iii) 1.97 (iv) 103 (v) 7.05 Which of these numbers are given to 2 significant figures?

  A (i) only

  B (ii) and (iii)

  C (iv) and (v)

  D (ii), (iii) and (v)

  E (i), (iv) and (v)

8 23.003 1670 1.067 23.6 0.038 How many of these numbers are written to 3 significant figures?

  A 1

  B 2

  C 3

  D 4

  E 5

9 3080   0.205   0.017   0.0461   20051
How many of these numbers are written to 3 significant figures?

A 1

B 2

C 3

D 4

E 5

10 What is the answer to 2.8 ÷ 0.003 given to 2 significant figures?

A 0.93

B 9.3

C 93

D 930

E 9300

11 What is the answer to 73 × 21 given to 2 significant figures?

A 1000

B 1400

C 1500

D 1600

E 2000

12 How many of the following numbers are written to 3 significant figures?
40605   406   40.6   0.406   0.046

A 4

B 3

C 2

D 1

E 0

13 How many significant figures are there in 0.002 004?

A 2

B 3

C 4

D 5

E 6

14 How many significant figures are there in 1060.07?

A 2

B 3

C 4

D 6

E 7

15 Which of the following is the value of 30.256 when written to 2 significant figures?

A 30

B 30.2

C 30.3

D 30.25

E 30.26

16 Which of the following is the value of 8.0649 when written to 1 significant figure?

A 8.07

B 8.06

C 8.1

D 8

E 8.0

14.2 Accuracy of measurements

1 What is the maximum difference between the highest and lowest value possible for a measurement given to the nearest centimetre?

A 0.5 cm

B 0.9 cm

C 0.99 cm

D 0.999 cm

E 1 cm

2 The width of a road is measured as 5 metres to the nearest metre.
What is the greatest possible width it could be?

A 5.4 m

B 5.49 m

C 5.5 m

D 5.499 m

E 5.4999 m

3 The weight of a pumpkin is 8 kg to the nearest kilogram. What is the actual weight, x kilograms, of the pumpkin?

A $7.5 \leqslant x < 8.5$

B $7.5 \leqslant x < 8.4$

C $7.51 \leqslant x < 8.49$

D $7.5 \leqslant x < 8.49$

E $7.51 \leqslant x < 8.5$

4 A pencil is 9 cm long when measured to the nearest millimetre. What is the least possible length of the pencil?

A 8.96 cm

B 8.95 cm

C 8.9 cm

D 8.51 cm

E 8.5 cm

5 A packet is weighed as 500 g to the nearest gram.
What is the most it could possibly weigh?

A 500.49 g

B 500.4999 g

C 500.5 g

D 504.9 g

E 505 g

6 The time is given as 1500 to the nearest hour.
What is the earliest the time could be?

A 1405

B 1430

C 1450

D 1505

E 1530

7 If the time is given as 1000 to the nearest hour, then the true time must be between

A 0950 and 1050

B 0930 and 1029

C 0931 and 1029

D 0930 and 1030

E 0955 and 1005

8 A measurement is given as 1 metre to the nearest centimetre.
What is the greatest possible error in this measurement?

A 0.49 cm

B 0.5 cm

C 0.9 cm

D 5 cm

E 0.5 m

15 Three-dimensional shapes (1)

15.2 Surface area of three-dimensional shapes

1 What is the total surface area of a cube with sides of 2 cm?

A 24 cm²

B 8 cm²

C 20 cm²

D 48 cm²

E 12 cm²

2 What is the total surface area of a cuboid of dimensions 3 cm by 5 cm by 8 cm?

A 120 cm²

B 143 cm²

C 103 cm²

D 158 cm²

E 134 cm²

3 What is the total surface area of this prism?

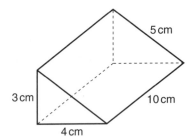

A 60 cm²

B 132 cm²

C 138 cm²

D 600 cm²

E 120 cm²

4 What is the total surface area of a cube of side of length 5 cm?

A 125 cm²

B 30 cm²

C 100 cm²

D 40 cm²

E 150 cm²

5 What is the total surface area of this prism?

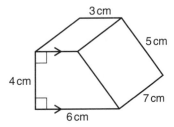

A 174 cm²

B 25 cm²

C 162 cm²

D 144 cm²

E 120 cm²

6 What is the total surface area of this prism?

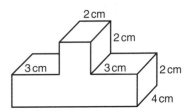

A 120 cm²

B 136 cm²

C 90 cm²

D 144 cm²

E 116 cm²

7 What is the total surface area of a cuboid of dimensions 4 cm by 5 cm by 7 cm?

  A 140 cm²

  B 105 cm²

  C 138 cm²

  D 166 cm²

  E 96 cm²

8 What is the total surface area of this prism?

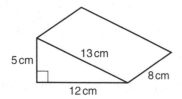

  A 300 cm²

  B 240 cm²

  C 6240 cm²

  D 3120 cm²

  E 600 cm²

9 What is the total surface area of this prism?

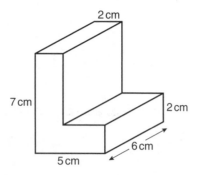

  A 96 cm²

  B 144 cm²

  C 210 cm²

  D 184 cm²

  E 160 cm²

10 What is the total surface area of a cube or side of length 8 cm?

  A 24 cm²

  B 384 cm²

  C 48 cm²

  D 512 cm²

  E 320 cm²

11 What is the total surface area of this square-based pyramid?

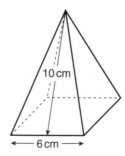

  A 276 cm²

  B 60 cm²

  C 240 cm²

  D 480 cm²

  E 156 cm²

12 What is the total surface area of a cuboid of dimensions 20 mm by 30 mm by 50 mm?

  A 3000 mm²

  B 1000 mm²

  C 6200 mm²

  D 4800 mm²

  E 3800 mm²

15.3 Coordinates in three dimensions

1 A cuboid is drawn on a 3-D grid.
What are the 3-D coordinates of point Q?

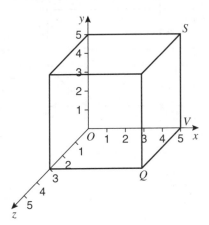

A $(0, 5, 5)$

B $(3, 0, 0)$

C $(5, 5, 5)$

D $(3, 5, 5)$

E $(5, 0, 3)$

2 A cuboid is drawn on a 3-D grid.
What are the coordinates of the midpoint
of line segment RP?

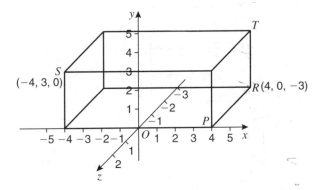

A $(4, 0, -1\frac{1}{2})$

B $(-1\frac{1}{2}, 2, 0)$

C $(4, -3, 0)$

D $(2, -1\frac{1}{2}, 0)$

E $(2, 1\frac{1}{2}, 0)$

3 G is the point $(2, -4, 6)$ and H is the point
$(4, -6, -2)$.
What are the coordinates of the midpoint
of the line segment GH?

A $(3, 2, 4)$

B $(6, -10, 4)$

C $(3, -5, 2)$

D $(3, 2, 4)$

E $(3, -2, -4)$

4 A cuboid is drawn on a 3-D grid.
What are the 3-D coordinates of point K?

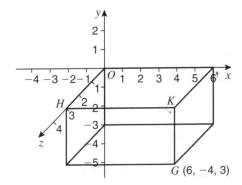

A $(3, 6, 0)$

B $(6, 0, 3)$

C $(6, 0, -4)$

D $(0, 6, -4)$

E $(0, 6, 3)$

5 P is the point $(1, -3, 4)$ and Q is the point
$(5, 7, -8)$.
What are the coordinates of the midpoint
of the line segment PQ?

A $(3, 2, -2)$

B $(3, 5, -6)$

C $(4, 4, -4)$

D $(3, 5, -2)$

E $(3, 2, -6)$

6 A cuboid is drawn on a 3-D grid.
What are the coordinates of the midpoint of the line segment SV?

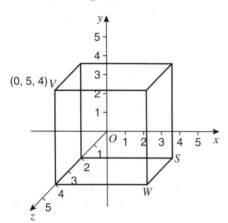

A $(5, 4, 0)$

B $(0, 4, 5)$

C $(2\frac{1}{2}, 2\frac{1}{2}, 3)$

D $(3, 2\frac{1}{2}, 2\frac{1}{2})$

E $(2\frac{1}{2}, 2\frac{1}{2}, 3)$

7 S is the point $(4, 5, -8)$ and T is the point $(-2, -1, -2)$.
What are the coordinates of the midpoint of the line segment ST?

A $(6, 6, -6)$

B $(-1, 2, -3)$

C $(1, 2, 3)$

D $(1, 2, -5)$

E $(2, 3, -4)$

8 A cuboid is drawn on a 3-D grid.
What are the 3-D coordinates of point T?

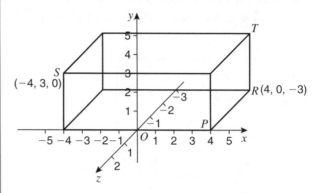

A $(-4, -3, 3)$

B $(0, 4, -3)$

C $(4, 3, -3)$

D $(0, 0, 3)$

E $(-4, 3, -3)$

9 A cuboid is drawn on a 3-D grid.
What are the 3-D coordinates of point W?

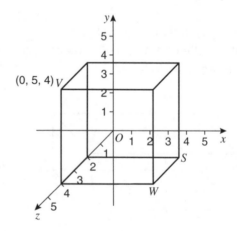

A $(4, 0, 5)$

B $(5, 2, 4)$

C $(4, 2, 5)$

D $(5, 0, 4)$

E $(5, 0, 4)$

10 K is the point $(5, -4, 2)$ and L is the point $(-3, 6, -4)$.
What are the coordinates of the midpoint of the line segment KL?

A $(4, 5, -3)$

B $(2, 2, -2)$

C $(-2, 5, 3)$

D $(2, 5, 3)$

E $(1, 1, -1)$

11 A cuboid is drawn on a 3-D grid.
What are the coordinates of the midpoint of the line segment HG?

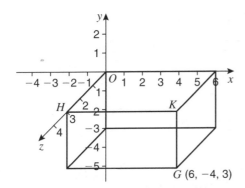

A $(3, 3, 2)$

B $(3, -2, 3)$

C $(3, -2, 3)$

D $(3, 0, -2)$

E $(3, 3, 0)$

12 A cuboid is drawn on a 3-D grid.
What are the coordinates of the midpoint of the line segment VQ?

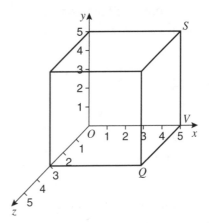

A $(2\frac{1}{2}, 1\frac{1}{2}, 0)$

B $(5, 1\frac{1}{2}, 0)$

C $(1\frac{1}{2}, 5, 0)$

D $(0, 2\frac{1}{2}, 1\frac{1}{2})$

E $(0, 5, 1\frac{1}{2})$

13 $A(0, 0, 4)$, $B(4, 6, 0)$ and $C(0, 8, 2)$ are three points.
M is the midpoint of AB.
What are the coordinates of the midpoint of CM?

A $(1, 5.5, 2)$

B $(2, 7, 3)$

C $(1, 11, 2)$

D $(1, 5.5, 3)$

E $(2, 5.5, 2)$

16 Indices and standard form

16.2 Standard form

1 What is the number 628 000 written in standard form?

    A 628×10^{-5}

    B 6.28×10^{6}

    C 6.28×10^{5}

    D 6.28×10^{3}

    E 62.8×10^{4}

2 Work out, in standard form, the value of the expression $3 \times 10^{5} \times 3 \times 10^{3}$

    A 9×10^{8}

    B 3×10^{12}

    C 6×10^{15}

    D 3×10^{8}

    E 9×10^{15}

3 What is the number 7.43×10^{5} written as an ordinary number?

    A 74 300 000

    B 0.000 0743

    C 7.430 00

    D 743 000

    E 74 300

4 Work out, in standard form, the value of the expression $3 \times 10^{4} \times 6 \times 10^{3}$

    A 18×10^{7}

    B 1.8×10^{12}

    C 1.8×10^{8}

    D 9×10^{7}

    E 1.8×10^{7}

5 Light travels at 9.5×10^{12} km per year. How far does light travel in 2000 years?

    A 19×10^{12}

    B 1.9×10^{15}

    C 19×10^{15}

    D 1.9×10^{12}

    E 1.9×10^{16}

6 What is the number 0.005 67 written in standard form?

    A 5.67×10^{12}

    B 5.67×10^{-3}

    C 56.7×10^{4}

    D 0.567×10^{-3}

    E 567×10^{5}

7 What is the number 2.31×10^{-4} written as an ordinary number?

    A 0.000 231

    B 23 100

    C 2.3100

    D 0.0231

    E −23 100

8 A proton has a mass of 1.7×10^{-24} grams. What is the total mass of 200 protons?

    A 34×10^{-22}

    B 3.4×10^{-26}

    C 34×10^{-26}

    D 3.4×10^{-22}

    E 3.4×10^{-24}

9 What is the number 4.53×10^7 written as an ordinary number?

 A 0.000 000 453

 B 453 000 000

 C 4.530 000 0

 D 0.004 53

 E 45 300 000

10 Work out, in standard form, the value of the expression $6 \times 10^5 \times 8 \times 10^7$

 A 48×10^{12}

 B 4.8×10^{13}

 C 48×10^{35}

 D 4.8×10^{12}

 E 4.8×10^{35}

11 What is the number 2.75×10^{-5} written as an ordinary number?

 A 275 000

 B 0.000 275

 C 0.000 027 5

 D $-0.000\,275$

 E $-275\,000$

12 What is the number 46 600 written in standard form?

 A 466×10^4

 B 4.66×10^{-4}

 C 4.66×10^2

 D 4.66×10^4

 E 4.66×10^{-1}

13 An electron has a mass of 9.1×10^{-31} grams. What is the total mass of 100 electrons?

 A 9.1×10^{-29}

 B 910×10^{-31}

 C 91×10^{-31}

 D 9.1×10^{-33}

 E 910×10^{-33}

14 What is the number 0.000 845 written in standard form?

 A 8.45×10^4

 B 8.45×10^{-3}

 C 845×10^{-6}

 D 84.5×10^{-4}

 E 8.45×10^{-4}

15 Work out, in standard form, the value of the expression $4 \times 10^{-3} \times 7 \times 10^8$

 A 2.8×10^5

 B 2.8×10^6

 C 28×10^5

 D 2.8×10^{-24}

 E 2.8×10^{-5}

16 The mass of the Earth is 5.8×10^{24} kg. The mass of Saturn is 100 times this. What is the mass of Saturn?

 A 5.8×10^{22}

 B 580×10^{24}

 C 5.8×10^{26}

 D 580×10^{26}

 E 580×10^{22}

17 Further factorising, simplifying and algebraic proof

17.1 Further factorising

1 Factorise $4x^2 - 16x - 9$

  A $(4x + 3)(x - 3)$

  B $(2x - 9)(2x + 1)$

  C $(2x - 3)(2x + 3)$

  D $(2x - 1)(2x + 9)$

  E $(4x + 1)(x - 9)$

2 Factorise $10x^2 - 11x - 6$

  A $(5x - 6)(2x + 1)$

  B $(10x + 1)(x - 6)$

  C $(2x - 3)(5x + 2)$

  D $(10x - 3)(x + 2)$

  E $(5x + 3)(2x - 2)$

3 Factorise $4x^2 - 20x + 25$

  A $(4x - 5)(x - 5)$

  B $(4x + 1)(x - 25)$

  C $(4x - 25)(x + 1)$

  D $(2x - 5)(2x - 5)$

  E $(2x + 5)(2x - 5)$

4 Factorise $9x^2 - 6x + 1$

  A $(9x - 1)(x + 1)$

  B $(9x + 1)(x - 1)$

  C $(3x + 1)(3x - 1)$

  D $(9x - 1)(x - 1)$

  E $(3x - 1)(3x - 1)$

5 Factorise $81x^2 + 90x + 25$

  A $(9x - 5)(9x - 5)$

  B $(81x + 5)(x + 5)$

  C $(27x - 1)(3x + 25)$

  D $(27x - 1)(3x - 25)$

  E $(9x + 5)(9x + 5)$

6 Factorise $30 + 7x - 2x^2$

  A $(30 + 2x)(1 - x)$

  B $(1 - 2x)(30 + x)$

  C $(3 - 2x)(10 + x)$

  D $(6 - x)(5 + 2x)$

  E $(6 - 2x)(5 + x)$

7 Factorise $2a^2 - ab - 6b^2$

  A $(2a + 3b)(a - 2b)$

  B $(2a - 3b)(a + 2b)$

  C $(2a - b)(a + 6b)$

  D $(2a + b)(a - 6b)$

  E $(2a - b)(a - 6b)$

8 Factorise $20y^2 - 11xy - 4x^2$

  A $(5y + 4x)(4y - x)$

  B $(5y - 4x)(4y + x)$

  C $(5y - 2x)(4y + 2x)$

  D $(10y - 2x)(2y + 2x)$

  E $(10y + x)(2y - 4x)$

9 Factorise $4x^2 + 12x + 9$

    A $(4x + 1)(x + 9)$

    B $(4x + 3)(x + 3)$

    C $(2x - 3)(2x - 3)$

    D $(2x + 3)(2x + 3)$

    E $(4x + 6)(x + 2)$

10 Factorise $9x^2 - 12xy - 5y^2$

    A $(3x + 5y)(3x - y)$

    B $(3x - 5y)(3x - y)$

    C $(3x + y)(3x - 5y)$

    D $(9x + y)(x - 5y)$

    E $(9x - y)(x + 5y)$

11 Factorise $18p^2 - 27pq - 5q^2$

    A $(9p + 5q)(2p - q)$

    B $(3p + 5q)(6p - q)$

    C $(9p + q)(2p - 5q)$

    D $(18p + q)(p - 5q)$

    E $(3p - 5q)(6p + q)$

12 Factorise $4x^2 - 4x + 1$

    A $(2x - 1)(2x - 1)$

    B $(2x + 1)(2x + 1)$

    C $(4x + 1)(x + 1)$

    D $(4x - 1)(x - 1)$

    E $(4x + 1)(x - 1)$

13 Factorise $4x^2 + 7xy + 3y^2$

    A $(4x + y)(x + 3y)$

    B $(2x + 3y)(2x + y)$

    C $(4x + 3y)(x + y)$

    D $(2x - y)(2x - 3y)$

    E $(4x - y)(4x - 3y)$

14 Factorise $10x^2 + 21x - 10$

    A $(2x + 5)(5x - 2)$

    B $(2x - 2)(5x + 5)$

    C $(2x - 5)(5x + 2)$

    D $(10x - 2)(x + 5)$

    E $(10x + 2)(x - 5)$

15 Factorise $16x^2 - 8xy - 3y^2$

    A $(4x + 3y)(4x - y)$

    B $(8x + y)(2x - 3y)$

    C $(8x - y)(2x + 3y)$

    D $(4x - 3y)(4x + y)$

    E $(16x - 3y)(x + y)$

16 Factorise $21x^2 + 34xy + 8y^2$

    A $(7x - 2y)(3x - 4y)$

    B $(7x + 2y)(3x + 4y)$

    C $(7x - 2y)(3x - 4y)$

    D $(7x + 2y)(3x + 4y)$

    E $(7x - y)(3x + 8y)$

17 Factorise $8x^2 - 2xy - 3y^2$

    A $(4x - 3y)(2x - y)$

    B $(4x + 3y)(2x - y)$

    C $(4x - 3y)(2x + y)$

    D $(x - 4y)(8x - 2y)$

    E $(4x + y)(2x - y)$

18 Circle geometry

18.2 Isosceles triangles

1 Here is a circle with centre O.
Angle $X = 40°$

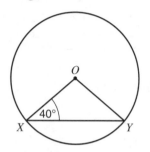

Diagram **NOT**
accurately drawn

Which of these is the size of angle Y?

A 100°

B 50°

C 40°

D 70°

E 140°

2 Here is a circle with centre O.
Angle $X = 40°$

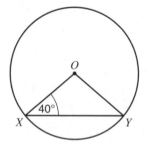

Diagram **NOT**
accurately drawn

Which of these is the size of angle O?

A 100°

B 50°

C 40°

D 70°

E 140°

3 Here is a circle with centre O.
Angle $O = 40°$

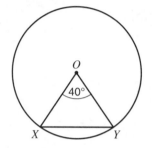

Diagram **NOT**
accurately drawn

Which of these is the size of angle X?

A 100°

B 50°

C 40°

D 70°

E 140°

4 Here is a circle with centre O.
Reflex angle $O = 290°$

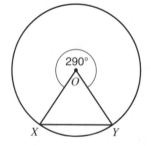

Diagram **NOT**
accurately drawn

Which of these is the size of angle Y?

A 110°

B 55°

C 35°

D 70°

E 140°

5 Here is a circle with centre O.
Angle $O = 50°$

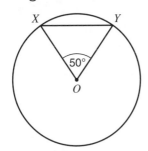

Diagram **NOT**
accurately drawn

Which of these is the size of angle Y?

A 130°

B 25°

C 65°

D 50°

E 165°

6 Here is a circle with centre O.
Angle $YOZ = 108°$

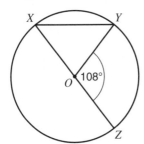

Diagram **NOT**
accurately drawn

Which of these is the size of angle Y?

A 108°

B 72°

C 36°

D 56°

E 54°

7 Here is a circle with centre O.
Angle $QRS = 140°$

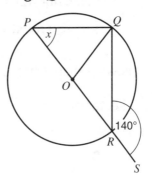

Diagram **NOT**
accurately drawn

Which of these is the size of the angle
marked x?

A 40°

B 70°

C 50°

D 100°

E 80°

8 Here is a circle with centre O.
Angle $Y = 40°$
Angle $Z = 15°$

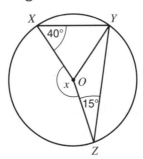

Diagram **NOT**
accurately drawn

Which of these is the size of the angle
marked x?

A 80°

B 90°

C 250°

D 100°

E 110°

Practice Paper 1

Answer ALL TWENTY FIVE questions

You must NOT use a calculator

1 Which one of the following shapes has exactly four sides with the same length?

Rhombus	Rectangle	Kite	Trapezium	Parallelogram
=	=	=	=	=
A	**B**	**C**	**D**	**E**

2 It costs Sean £26 for each weekly train ticket he buys.
Sean buys n tickets during a school term.
Find an expression, in terms of n, for the cost, in pounds, of buying the tickets.

n	$n + 26$	$2600n$	$26n$	$\dfrac{n}{26}$
=	=	=	=	=
A	**B**	**C**	**D**	**E**

3 Find the lowest common multiple (LCM) of 15 and 50

3	5	15	150	750
=	=	=	=	=
A	**B**	**C**	**D**	**E**

4 Katy buys 26 mathematical instrument sets for £5.65 each. What is the total cost?

£350.30	£45.20	£146.90	£39.58	£158.20
=	=	=	=	=
A	**B**	**C**	**D**	**E**

5 A square piece of card measures 1 m by 1 m.
A hole 30 cm by 20 cm is cut out of it.
What is the area, in cm², of card left?

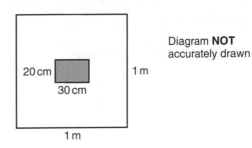

Diagram **NOT**
accurately drawn

20 cm | 1 m
30 cm
1 m

599	9400	40	400	5000
=	=	=	=	=
A	**B**	**C**	**D**	**E**

6

$Q(5, 3)$

Diagram **NOT**
accurately drawn

$P(-1, 1)$

The coordinates of the midpoint of the line PQ are

$(4, 4)$	$(4, 2)$	$(3, 2)$	$(3, 1)$	$(2, 2)$
=	=	=	=	=
A	**B**	**C**	**D**	**E**

7 Here are the first five terms of an arithmetic sequence.

10   18   26   34   42

What is the expression, in terms of n, for the nth term of the sequence?

$n - 8$	$8n - 2$	$n + 8$	$8n + 2$	$8n$
=	=	=	=	=
A	**B**	**C**	**D**	**E**

8 Simplify $8p - 5q - 3p + 3q$

$11p + 8q$	$5p + 2q$	$3p + 2q$	$5p - 2q$	$11p - 2q$
=	=	=	=	=
A	**B**	**C**	**D**	**E**

9 Factorise $t^2 + 4tw$

$4t$	$t^2(t + 4w)$	$t(t + 4w)$	$t + 4w$	$4t^2$
=	=	=	=	=
A	**B**	**C**	**D**	**E**

10 Ruth takes $3\frac{1}{2}$ hours to travel 140 km in her car.
What is her average speed?

50 km/h	60 km/h	35 km/h	49 km/h	40 km/h
=	=	=	=	=
A	**B**	**C**	**D**	**E**

11 Which of the following is equivalent to the expression $(x + 5)(x + 9)$

$x^2 + 14x + 45$	$x^2 + 14x + 14$	$x^2 + 45x + 45$	$x^2 - 4x + 45$	$x^2 + 45x + 14$
=	=	=	=	=
A	**B**	**C**	**D**	**E**

12

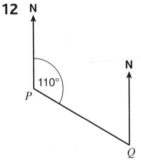

Diagram **NOT** accurately drawn

The bearing of Q from P is 110°.
What is the bearing of P from Q?

070°	290°	190°	180°	310°
=	=	=	=	=
A	**B**	**C**	**D**	**E**

13 Given that $156 \times 37 = 5772$, find the value of $57.72 \div 3.7$

0.0156	0.156	1.56	15.6	156
A	B	C	D	E

14 What is the highest common factor (HCF) of 18 and 60?

3	6	1080	18	12
A	B	C	D	E

15 Which of the following is the best estimate for the expression $\dfrac{403 \times 8.1}{0.22}$?

3200	1600	32 000	640	16 000
A	B	C	D	E

16 Factorise $x^2 - 2x - 15$

$(x + 2)(x - 5)$	$(x - 3)(x - 5)$	$(x + 3)(x - 5)$	$(x - 3)(x + 5)$	$(x - 2)(x - 5)$
A	B	C	D	E

17 Work out $3\frac{3}{4} \times 1\frac{1}{2}$

$4\frac{1}{4}$	$\frac{3}{8}$	$5\frac{1}{2}$	$3\frac{3}{8}$	$5\frac{5}{8}$
A	B	C	D	E

18 What is the total surface area of a cube with sides of length 3 cm?

54 cm²	18 cm²	27 cm²	48 cm²	9 cm²
A	B	C	D	E

19 Factorise completely $3k^2 + 12k^5$

$3k^2(k + 3k^2)$	$3(k^2 + 4k^4)$	$3k(k + 3k^3)$	$3k^2(1 + 4k^3)$	$k^2(k + 4k^3)$
=	=	=	=	=
A	**B**	**C**	**D**	**E**

20 The length of a piece of rope is 457 mm, correct to the nearest mm.
What is the maximum length that the piece of rope could be?

457.4 mm	457.5 mm	457 mm	458 mm	456.5 mm
=	=	=	=	=
A	**B**	**C**	**D**	**E**

21 Write the number 4810 in standard form.

4.81×10^{-1}	481×10^{-3}	4.81×10^3	4.81×10^{-4}	481×10^3
=	=	=	=	=
A	**B**	**C**	**D**	**E**

22 Expand and simplify $(3x - 2)^2$

$9x^2 + 4$	$9x^2 + 6x + 4$	$9x^2 - 4$	$9x^2 + 12x - 4$	$9x^2 - 12x + 4$
=	=	=	=	=
A	**B**	**C**	**D**	**E**

23 Factorise $6x^2 - 13xy + 5y^2$

$(3x - 5y)(2x - y)$	$(6x - y)(x - 5y)$	$(3x + 5y)(2x - y)$
=	=	=
A	**B**	**C**

$(x + 5y)(6x - y)$	$(2x - y)(3x - 5y)$
=	=
D	**E**

24 P and Q are two points on a 3-D coordinate grid.
Point P is $(-8, 6, -4)$, point Q is $(6, -4, 2)$.
What are the coordinates of the midpoint of the line PQ?

$(-1, 1, -1)$	$(-2, 2, -2)$	$(1, 1, 1)$	$(2, 2, 2)$	$(-1, -1, -1)$
=	=	=	=	=
A	**B**	**C**	**D**	**E**

25 An empty container has a capacity of 1000 litres.
The container is filled with water.
It takes $12\frac{1}{2}$ minutes to fill the container.
What is the rate, in litres per second, at which the container is filled?

12.5	80	830	25	60
=	=	=	=	=
A	**B**	**C**	**D**	**E**

Practice Paper 2
Answer ALL TWENTY FIVE questions
You must NOT use a calculator

1 Selena travelled 150 miles in 3 hours.
What was her average speed in miles per hour (mph)?

450 mph	50 mph	45 mph	4.5 mph	55 mph
A	B	C	D	E

2

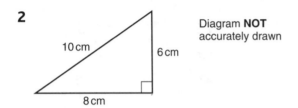

Diagram **NOT** accurately drawn

10 cm   6 cm

8 cm

What is the area of this triangle?

48 cm²	240 cm²	24 cm²	14 cm²	480 cm²
A	B	C	D	E

3 Which of the following is the best estimate for the value of $\dfrac{89.9 \times 30.2}{5.01 + 3.89}$?

30	40	400	300	3000
A	B	C	D	E

4 Bags of crisps cost 35 pence each.
Rani buys b bags of crisps.

What is the expression, in terms of b, for the total cost?

b	$\dfrac{b}{35}$	$35b + 35$	$\dfrac{35}{b}$	$35b$
A	B	C	D	E

5 What is $5a + 2b + a - 4b$ written in its simplest form?

$5a + 6b$	$11ab$	$4ab$	$6a - 2b$	$6a + 2b$
=	=	=	=	=
A	**B**	**C**	**D**	**E**

6 What is the lowest common multiple (LCM) of 30 and 45?

15	90	1350	135	5
=	=	=	=	=
A	**B**	**C**	**D**	**E**

7 Given that $7.2 \times 15.9 = 114.48$, what is the value of 0.72×1590?

0.11448	1.1448	11.448	1144.8	11448
=	=	=	=	=
A	**B**	**C**	**D**	**E**

8 Factorise $x^2 - 16x$

$x(x - 16x)$	$x(x - 16)$	$x(x^2 - 16x)$	$(x + 4)(x - 4)$	$2(x - 8)$
=	=	=	=	=
A	**B**	**C**	**D**	**E**

9 Expand $(x + 5)(x - 4)$

$x^2 - 9x - 20$	$x^2 - 20$	$2x + 1$	$x^2 - x - 20$	$x^2 + x - 20$
=	=	=	=	=
A	**B**	**C**	**D**	**E**

10 Here are the first five terms of an arithmetic sequence.

　　3　　8　　13　　18　　23

Which of the following is an expression for the nth term of this sequence?

$5n + 3$	$5n - 2$	$n + 5$	$5n$	$n - 2$
=	=	=	=	=
A	**B**	**C**	**D**	**E**

11

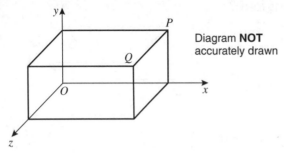

Diagram **NOT** accurately drawn

The point Q has coordinates $(5, 2, 3)$.
What are the coordinates of the point P?

$(3, 5, 0)$	$(5, 2, 0)$	$(3, 0, 2)$	$(0, 2, 3)$	$(3, 2, 5)$
A	B	C	D	E

12 R is the point with coordinates $(7, 1)$
S is the point with coordinates $(2, 5)$

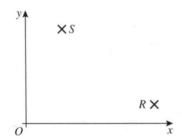

Which are the coordinates of the midpoint of the line RS?

$(5, -4)$	$(9, 6)$	$(7, 5)$	$(4\frac{1}{2}, 3)$	$(1, 2)$
A	B	C	D	E

13 Expand $5(4x - 3)$

$20x + 15$	$9x - 8$	$5x$	$20x - 15$	$35x$
A	B	C	D	E

14 What is 7.26×10^{-3} as an ordinary number?

7.260 00	726 000	7260	0.000 726	0.007 26
=	=	=	=	=
A	**B**	**C**	**D**	**E**

15 Here is a cuboid.

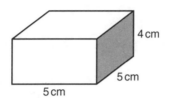

4 cm

5 cm

5 cm

Diagram **NOT** accurately drawn

What is the total surface area of the cuboid?

130 cm²	50 cm²	100 cm²	150 cm²	80 cm²
=	=	=	=	=
A	**B**	**C**	**D**	**E**

16

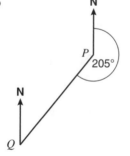

Diagram **NOT** accurately drawn

The bearing of Q from P is 205°
What is the bearing of P from Q?

025°	115°	030°	155°	335°
=	=	=	=	=
A	**B**	**C**	**D**	**E**

17 What is the value of $\frac{3}{10} \div \frac{4}{5}$?

$\frac{6}{25}$	$\frac{1}{5}$	$\frac{1}{8}$	$\frac{3}{8}$	$\frac{8}{3}$
=	=	=	=	=
A	**B**	**C**	**D**	**E**

18 Factorise completely $12p^2 - 9pr$

$p(12p - 9r)$	$3(4p^2 - 3pr)$	$3p(4 - 3r)$	$3p(p - 3r)$	$3p(4p - 3r)$
=	=	=	=	=
A	**B**	**C**	**D**	**E**

19 What is 565 000 in standard form?

5.65	5.65×10^{-3}	5.65×10^5	5065×10^3	5.65×10^{-5}
=	=	=	=	=
A	**B**	**C**	**D**	**E**

20 Expand $(3x - 2)(2x - 4)$

$6x^2 - 16x + 8$	$6x^2 + 8$	$6x^2 - 8$	$2x^2 - 16x + 8$	$2x^2 + 6x + 8$
=	=	=	=	=
A	**B**	**C**	**D**	**E**

21 Water flows from a container at a constant rate of 0.5 litres per second. How long does it take to empty if the container holds 90 litres of water?

4.5 minutes	18 seconds	3 minutes	45 seconds	9 minutes
=	=	=	=	=
A	**B**	**C**	**D**	**E**

22 One of the factors of $6x^2 - x - 15$ is $(2x + 3)$, what is the other factor?

$(3x + 5)$	$(3x - 12)$	$3(x - 5)$	$(x - 5)$	$(3x - 5)$
=	=	=	=	=
A	**B**	**C**	**D**	**E**

23 The length of a piece of string is 19 cm, correct to the nearest centimetre.
What is the greatest possible length the piece of string could be?

18.95	18.5	19.5	19.4	19.05
=	=	=	=	=
A	**B**	**C**	**D**	**E**

24 A cuboid is shown on a 3-D grid.

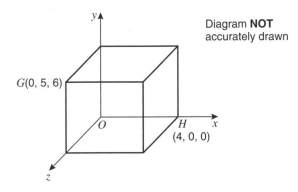

Diagram **NOT**
accurately drawn

The point G has coordinates $(0, 5, 6)$
The point H has coordinates $(4, 0, 0)$

Which of the following represents the coordinates of the midpoint of the line segment GH?

$(4, 5, 6)$	$(5, 4, 6)$	$(2, 2\frac{1}{2}, 3)$	$(2, 2\frac{1}{2}, 3)$	$(3, 2, 2\frac{1}{2})$
=	=	=	=	=
A	**B**	**C**	**D**	**E**

25 Expand and simplify $(3x - 4)^2$

$-x^2$	$9x^2 - 24x + 16$	$9x^2 + 16$	$9x^2 - 16$	$9x^2 + 24x + 16$
=	=	=	=	=
A	**B**	**C**	**D**	**E**